Contents

Differentiation of topics for 3 levels of ability

To differentiate the learning activities, the games have been colour coded according to the amount of French words that appear in the games. "Vert" is for the lower ability group, "jaune" is for the middle ability group, and "rouge" is for the higher ability group.

	vert	jaune	rouge
Pet animals	un chat un chien un poisson un serpent	un chat un chien un poisson un serpent un lapin un cheval	un chat un chien un poisson un serpent un lapin un cheval un oiseau une tortue une souris
Colours	rouge bleu vert jaune	rouge bleu vert jaune marron rose blanc noir	rouge bleu vert jaune marron rose blanc noir violet gris orange argent
Numbers	un deux trois quatre cinq	un deux trois quatre cinq six sept huit neuf dix	un deux trois quatre cinq six sept huit neuf dix onze douze
Fruit	un kiwi un melon une orange une banane	un kiwi un melon une orange une pomme une banane une fraise	un kiwi un melon une orange une pomme une banane une fraise un citron une poire des cerises
Drinks	un coca un jus d'orange une limonade une eau minérale	un coca un jus d'orange une limonade une eau minérale un café un thé	un coca un coca light un jus d'orange un jus de pomme une limonade une eau minérale un thé un café
Food	le poisson les pommes frites les pâtes le gâteau	le poulet le poisson la salade les pommes frites les pâtes le gâteau	le poulet le poisson la salade les pommes frites le fromage le gâteau les légumes les pâtes
Clothes	un jean un t-shirt un pull un manteau	un jean un t-shirt un pull un manteau un short une jupe	un jean un t-shirt un pull un manteau un short une jupe une casquette une robe un pantalon
Sport	le tennis le football le rugby le mini-golf le ping-pong le badminton	le tennis le rugby le football le mini-golf le ping-pong le badminton la natation le basket le karaté	le tennis le rugby le football le mini-golf le ping-pong le badminton l'équitation la natation le cyclisme le basket le karaté la gymnastique

Teachers note: see page 75 for pair work activities using the mini cards, and page 77 for class activities using the mini cards.

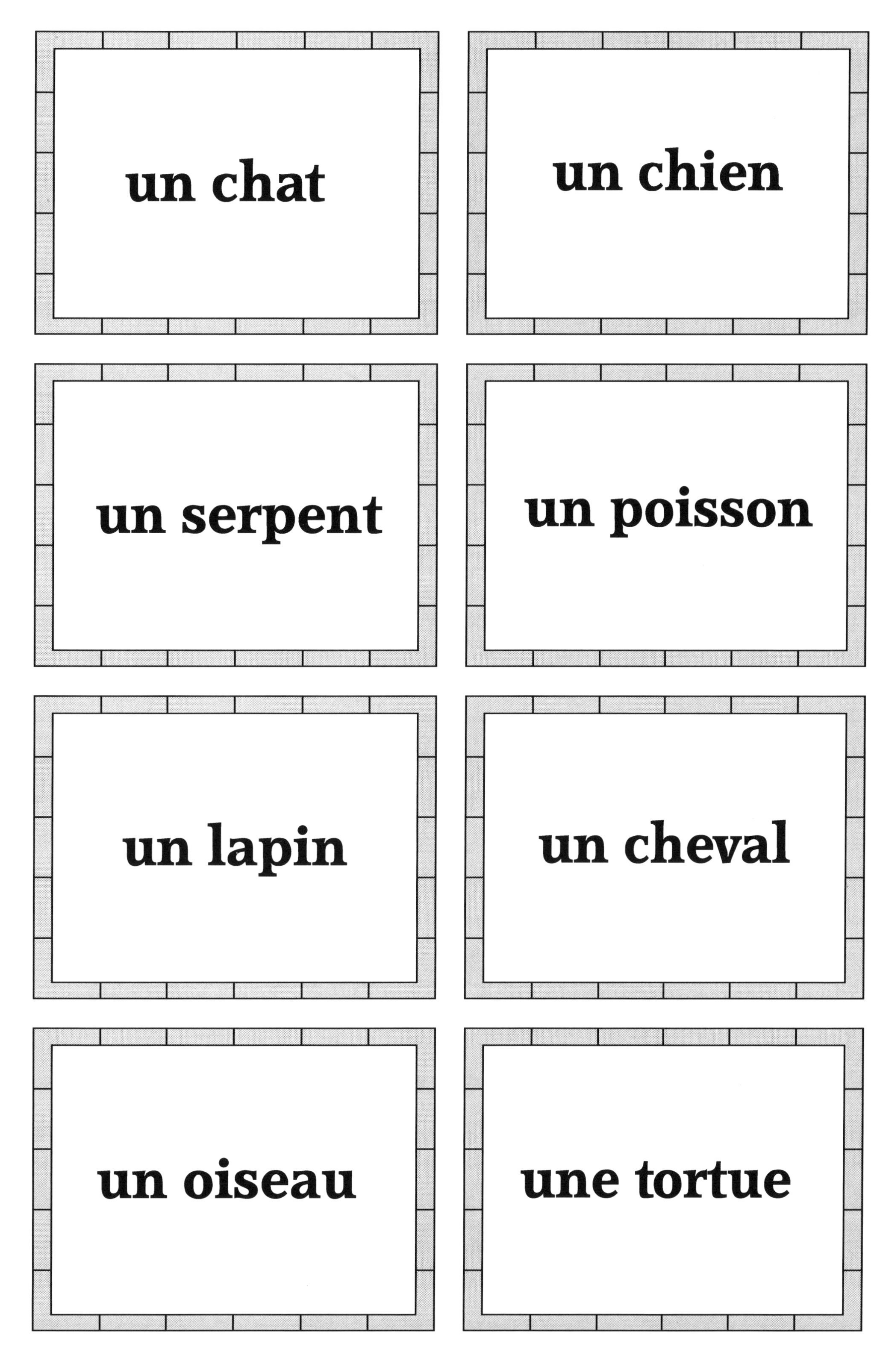

Teachers note: Photocopy this page (on card if possible), then make 8 cards by cutting round the cards. If you use card of **3 or 4 different colours** it is easier to separate the sets when handing them out to the class.

Can I say 4 animals in French?

Start at "**Départ**", roll the dice and count that number of spaces. Say the animal you land on in French. Take turns to roll the dice. To win, arrive first at "Arrivée."

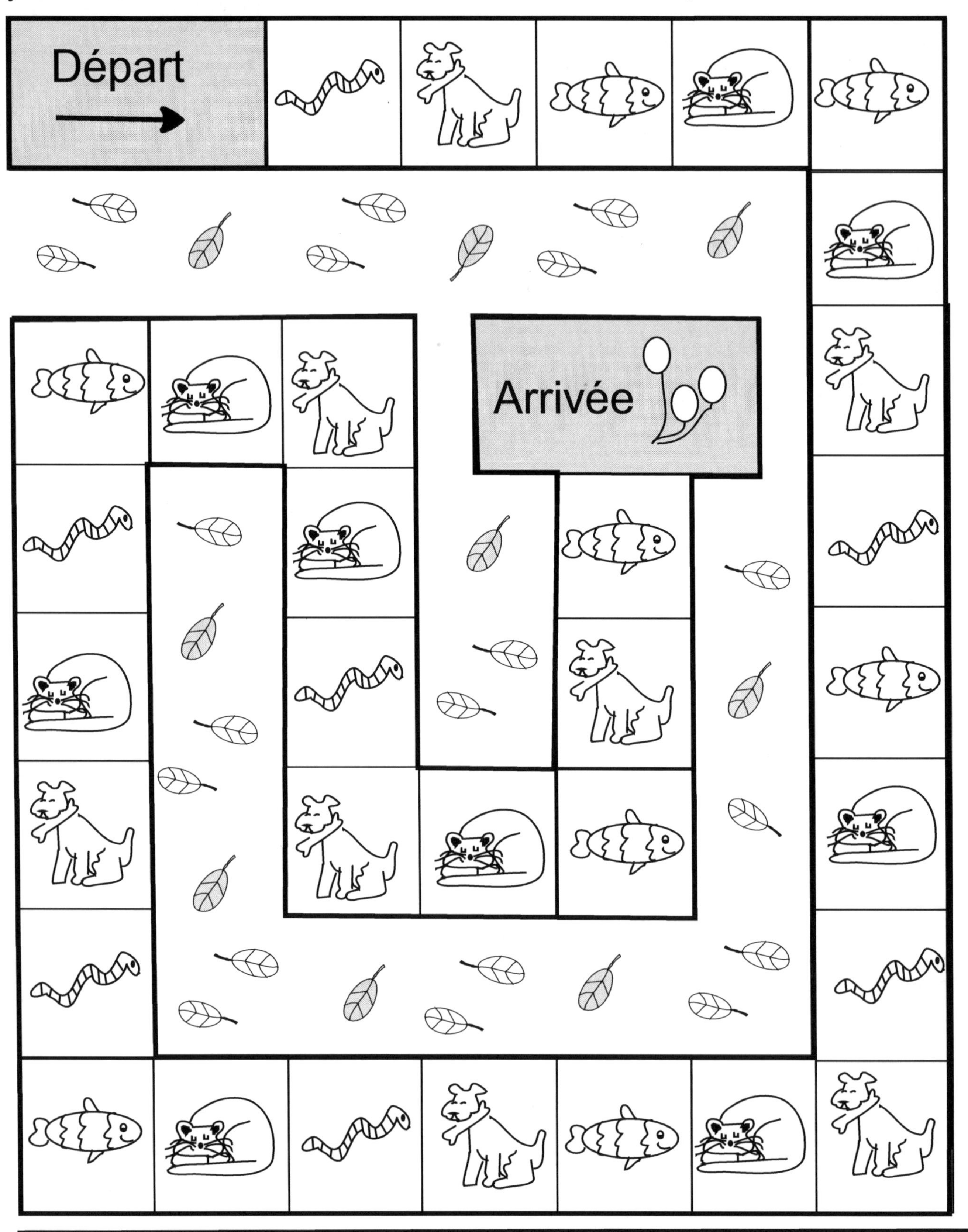

un poisson

un chien

un chat

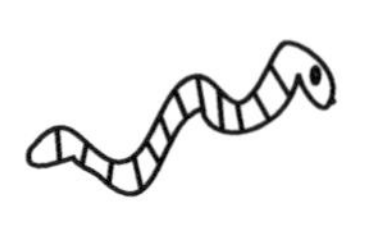
un serpent

Can I say 4 animals & 1 to 5 in French?

Each person / team needs 5 coloured counters or cubes of one colour (or a set of noughts or a set of crosses). Say the French word for the animal or number as you place your counter. To win you have to get 3 in a row (vertically, horizontally or diagonally).

un poisson un chien un chat un serpent

---

1 = un 2 = deux 3 = trois 4 = quatre 5 = cinq

Can I say 6 animals in French?

Start at **Départ**, roll the dice and count that number of spaces. Say the animal you land on in French. Take turns to roll the dice. To win, arrive first at **Arrivée.**

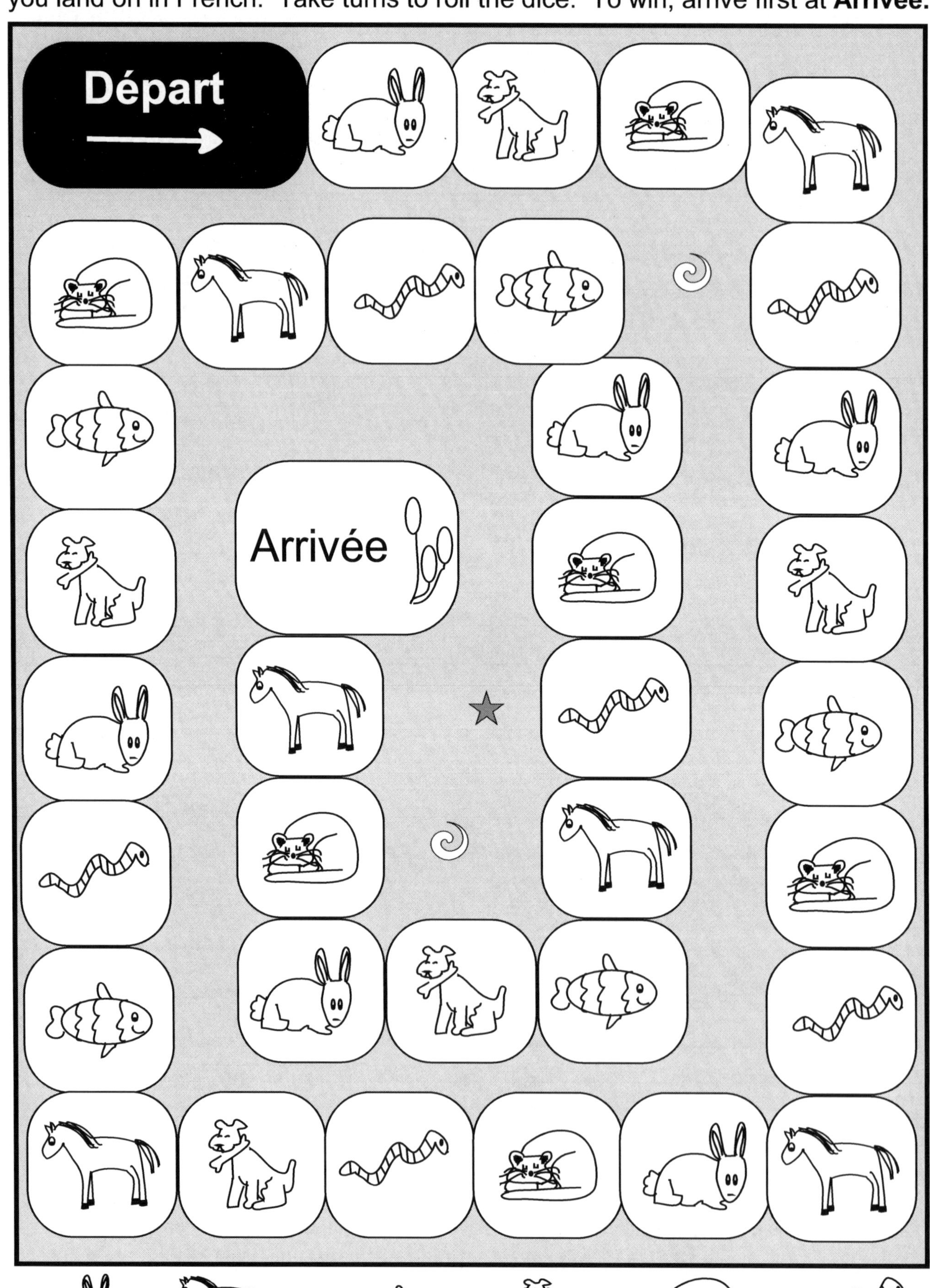

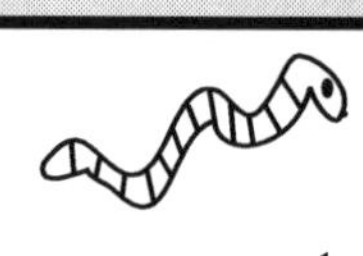

un lapin un cheval un poisson un chien un chat un serpent

Can I say 6 animals & 1-10 in French?

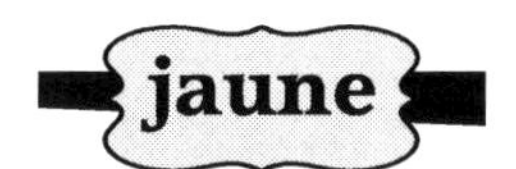

Each person / team needs 5 coloured counters or cubes of one colour (or a set of noughts or a set of crosses). Say the French word for the animal or number as you place your counter. To win you have to get 3 in a row (vertically, horizontally or diagonally).

2 = deux   4 = quatre   7 = sept

un lapin

un cheval

un poisson

un chien

un chat

un serpent

Can I say 9 animals in French?

Each person / team needs 15 coloured counters or cubes of one colour.

Say the French word for the animal as you place your counter or cube.
To win you have to get **4 in a row** (vertically, horizontally or diagonally).

un lapin

un cheval

un poisson

un chien

un chat

un serpent

un oiseau

une souris

une tortue

Can I say 9 animals in French? - Pupil A

With an adult present, cut out a set of **dominoes** by cutting along the dotted lines. In pairs, take turns to put a card down by matching a word to a picture or vice versa. If you cannot match a card, miss a turn. The winner is the person to either use all their cards, or use as many cards as possible.

Can I say 9 animals in French? - Pupil B rouge

With an adult present, cut out a set of **dominoes** by cutting along the dotted lines. In pairs, take turns to put a card down by matching a word to a picture or vice versa. If you cannot match a card, miss a turn. The winner is the person to either use all their cards, or use as many cards as possible.

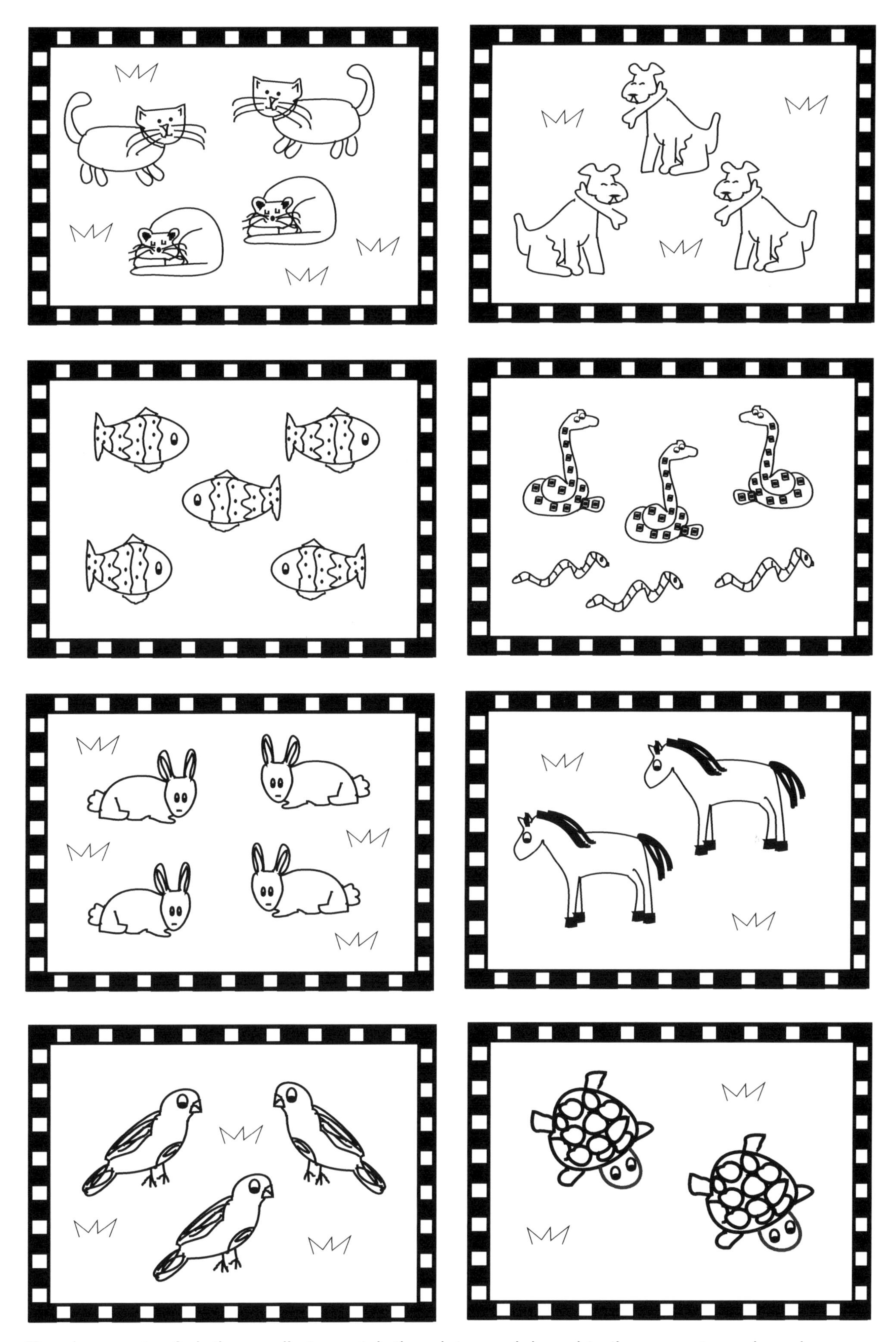

Teachers note: Ask the pupils to match the picture mini card to the correct word card.
See page 75 for pair work activities using the mini cards, and page 77 for class activities.

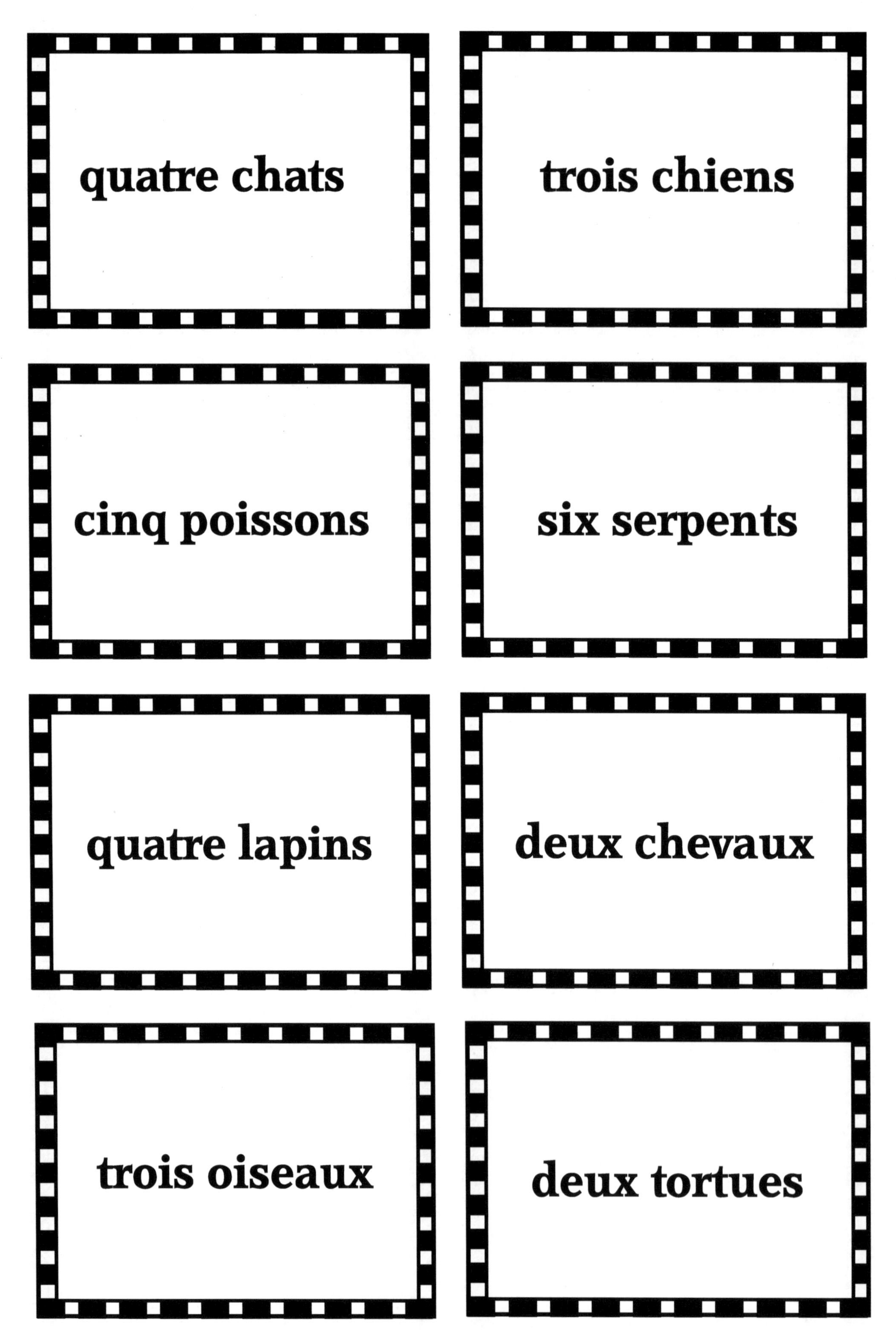

Teachers note: Photocopy this page (on card if possible), then make 8 cards by cutting round the cards. If you use card of **3 or 4 different colours** it is easier to separate the sets when handing them out to the class.

Making sentences with pet animals

When the pupils play the games, they could either practise just the vocabulary for the topic, or they could say a whole sentence. The pupils could write the phrase being practised on a mini whiteboard in front of them, or you could write the phrase on the IWB or whiteboard in the classroom.

Here are some ideas of the sentences you could instruct a group, or the whole class to practise for the pet animal topic:

1) **Saying if you have a pet**: J'ai = I have e.g. J'ai un chat.

2) **Asking a friend if they have a particular animal:** Tu as .....? (Do you have...?) e.g. Tu as un chien? Tu as un lapin?

3) **Describing the colour of the animals:** Ask the pupils to invent a colour for each of the pets, and say the colour after the French word for the animal. The games can be coloured in by the pupils. e.g. un chien marron, un lapin gris

4) **C'est grand ou c'est petit?**: Ask the pupils to decide if the animal is big or small, and say either **grand** (big) or **petit** (small) before the French word for the animal. e.g. un petit chat, un grand serpent

5) **Saying that you would like a particular animal**:
Je voudrais avoir ....(I would like to have .....) e.g. Je voudrais avoir un chat.

6) **Saying that you used to have a particular animal:** J'avais ... (I used to have...) e.g. J'avais une tortue. J'avais un poisson.

7) **Talking about which pets you like**: Tell the pupils that for saying if they like a particular animal they need to say the word in the plural. There is a photocopiable list of the animals in the plural in the word list section. The **s** at the end of the words in the plural is a silent **s**. There are 2 irregular plurals in the pet animals word list: oiseau becomes **oiseaux**, cheval becomes **chevaux**.

J'aime = I like e.g. J'aime les chats.

Je n'aime pas = I don't like e.g. Je n'aime pas les chiens.

J'adore = I love e.g. J'adore les poissons.

Je déteste = I hate e.g. Je déteste les souris.

Je préfère = I prefer e.g. Je préfère les chevaux.

8) **Saying if you have several pets**: J'ai trois lapins. J'ai cinq poissons.
Ask the pupils to change un to another number and to pretend they have this amount of the animals pictured. To do this, they could take turns to turn over the pictures for the pet animal mini cards, and roll one or two dice to see how many animals to say.

bleu

jaune

rouge

vert

blanc

marron

noir

rose

Making sentences with colours

As the pupils play the colour games they could say what colours they like:

J'aime (I like) J'aime le bleu. J'aime l'argent.

Je n'aime pas (I don't like) Je n'aime pas le jaune.

To vary their language, they could use the following phrases:
J'adore (I love) J'adore le violet.
Je déteste (I hate) Je déteste le marron.
Je préfère (I prefer) Je préfère le rouge. Je préfère l'orange.
Ma couleur préférée, c'est le (My favourite colour is) Ma couleur préférée, c'est le rose.

(In French the word **le** is needed after the above phrases and before the colour. **Le** is shortened to **l'** before orange as the word orange starts with a vowel.)

For a conversation, it is important to know how to ask questions. The pupils could also play the colour games and practise forming a question:
Tu aimes.....? = Do you like....? Tu aimes le rouge?

Teacher's note: The children could colour the mini cards / games before playing the games.

Can I say 4 colours in French?

Start at "**Départ**", roll the dice and count that number of spaces.
Say the colour you land on in French. To win, arrive first at "Arrivée."

Can I say 4 colours in French?

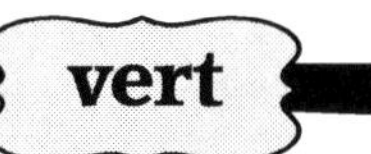

Roll two dice and find the coordinate by counting along the bottom for the first dice, and up the side for the second dice. Say the colour of the object in French for the coordinate to get a point e.g. 3, 2 = jaune. The winner is the person or team who gets the most points.

6

5

4

3

2

1

1 2 3 4 5 6

rouge

bleu

jaune

vert

Can I say 8 colours in French?

Start at “Départ”, roll the dice and count that number of squares. If the final square has the bottom of the ladder in it go up it, or if it has the head of a snake go down it. Say the colour of the object you land on in French. To win, arrive first at "Arrivée."

Can I say 8 colours in French?

Roll two dice and find the coordinate by counting along the bottom for the first dice, and up the side for the second dice. Say the colour of the object in French for the coordinate to get a point, e.g 4,3 = blanc. The winner Is the person or team who gets the most points.

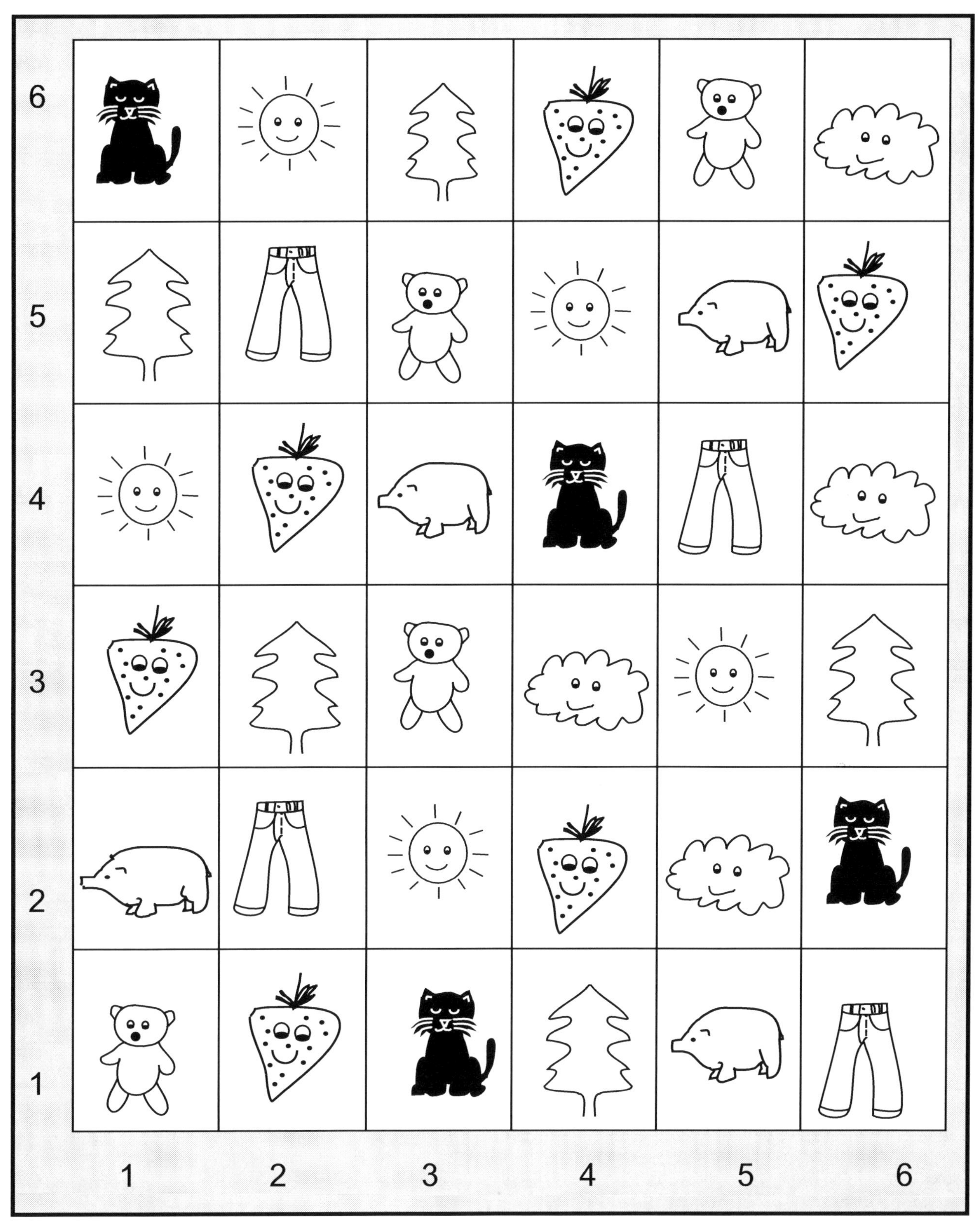

rouge

bleu

orange

vert

noir

marron

gris

rose

violet

Can I say 12 colours in French?

rouge

Start at "**Départ**", roll the dice and count that number of spaces. Say the colour you land on in French. Take turns to roll the dice. To win, arrive first at "Arrivée."

Can I say 12 colours in French?

Roll two dice and find the coordinate by counting along the bottom for the first dice, and up the side for the second dice. Say the colour in French for the object in the coordinate to get a point, e.g 6,3 = vert. The winner is the person or team who gets the most points.

jaune blanc argent

rouge

bleu

orange

vert

noir

marron

gris

rose

violet

Teachers note: Ask the pupils to match the picture mini card to the correct word card.
See page 75 for pair work activities using the mini cards, and page 77 for class activities.

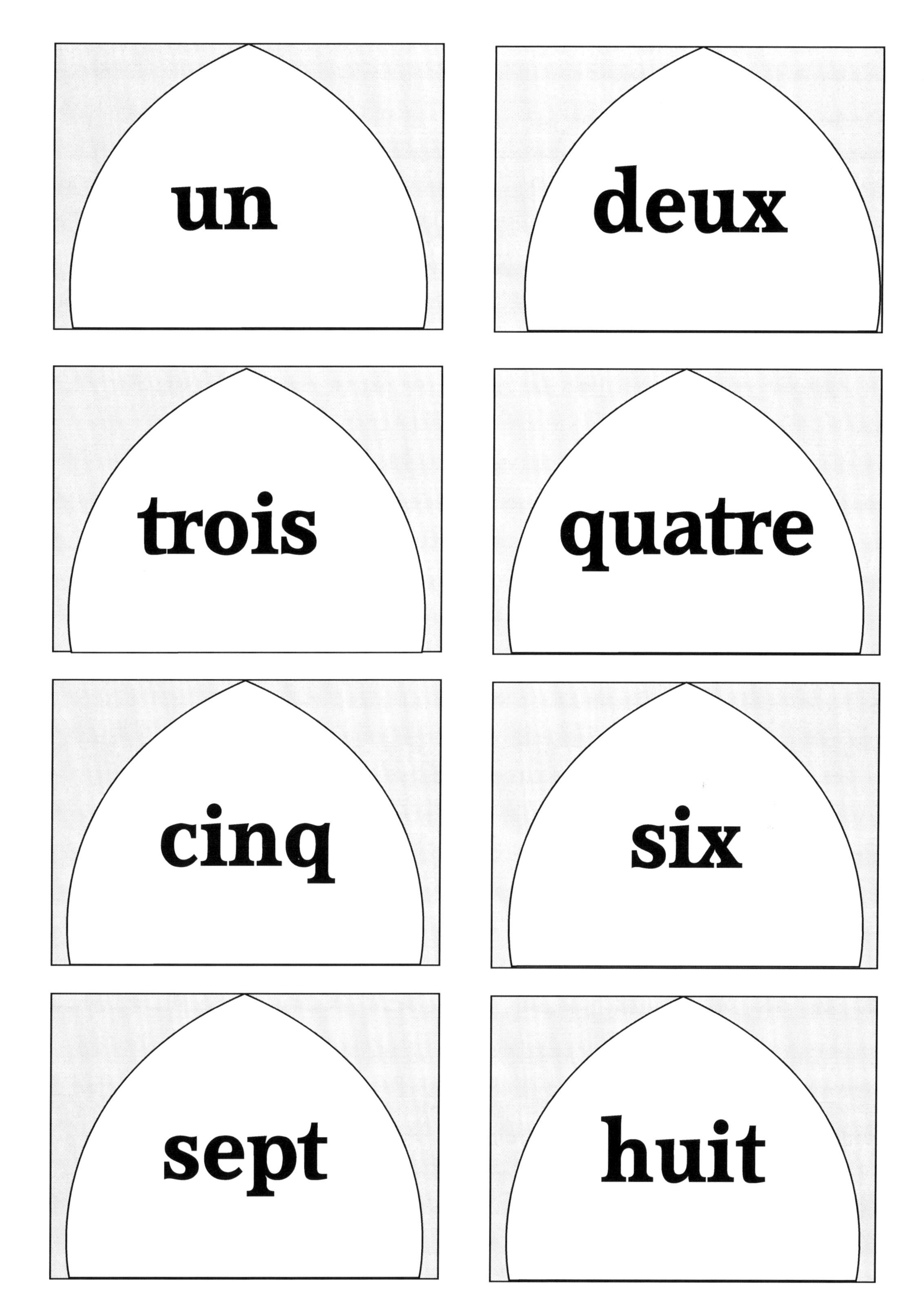

Teachers note: Photocopy this page (on card if possible), then make 8 cards by cutting round the cards. If you use card of **3 or 4 different colours** it is easier to separate the sets when handing them out to the class.

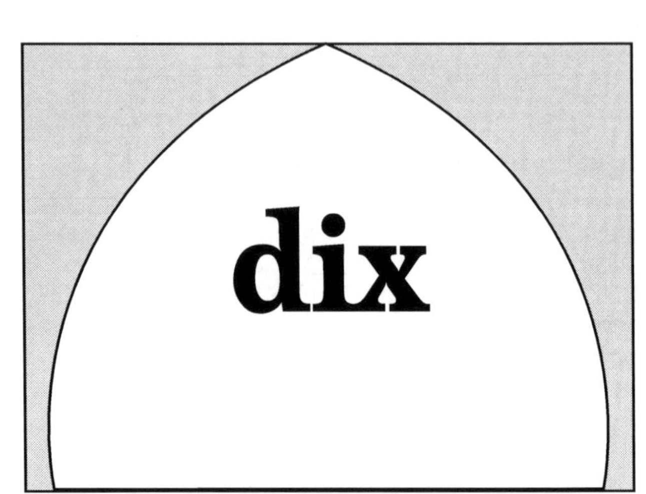

Making sentences with numbers

1) **Asking for quantities of things:** Tell the pupils that if they wanted to ask for a particular quantity of something in a shop they would have to say the number of items they wanted, and then add **s'il vous plaît** (please) at the end. The pupils could play the number games by adding **s'il vous plaît** after the number.

2) **Saying how old you are**: Teach the phrase **J'ai.....ans** (I am ..... years old) Ask the pupils to play the number games, but rather than just say the number, they are to say the corresponding age for each number they have in the games.

3) **Saying quantities of certain objects:** The pupils could also pretend to count things, for example **citrons** (lemons). As they play the games they say the number they see before the word citron. E.g. trois citrons. The final s in citrons is silent.

Can I say 5 numbers in French?

vert

Start at "**Départ**", roll the dice and count that number of spaces.
Say the number you land on in French. To win, arrive first at "Arrivée."

Arrivée 5 3 1 4

2

1 3 5 4 3

5 4 5

4 2 3 2

2 1 4

1 5 2 5 3

5

3 4 1 5 4 1

5

Départ 5 2 3 2

1 = un 2 = deux 3 = trois 4 = quatre 5 = cinq

Can I say 1 - 5 in French?

vert

Each person / team needs 5 coloured counters or cubes of one colour (or a set of noughts or a set of crosses). Say the French word for the number as you cover it with your counter.
To win you have to get 3 in a row (vertically, horizontally or diagonally).

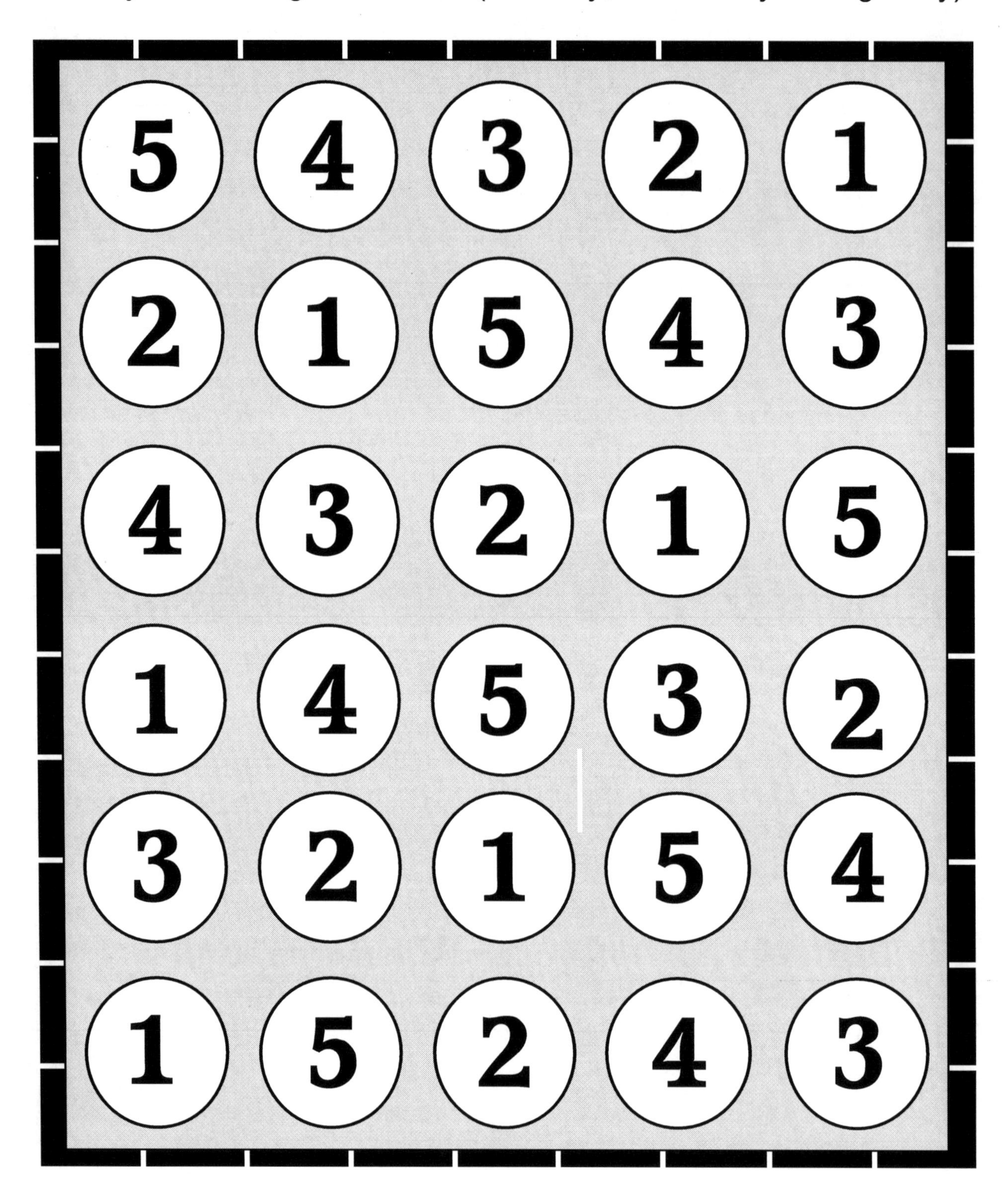

1 = un   2 = deux   3 = trois   4 = quatre   5 = cinq

Can I say 9 numbers in French?

Each person / team needs 5 coloured counters or cubes of one colour (or a set of noughts or a set of crosses).

Say the French word for the number as you cover it with your counter. To win you have to get 3 in a row (vertically, horizontally or diagonally).

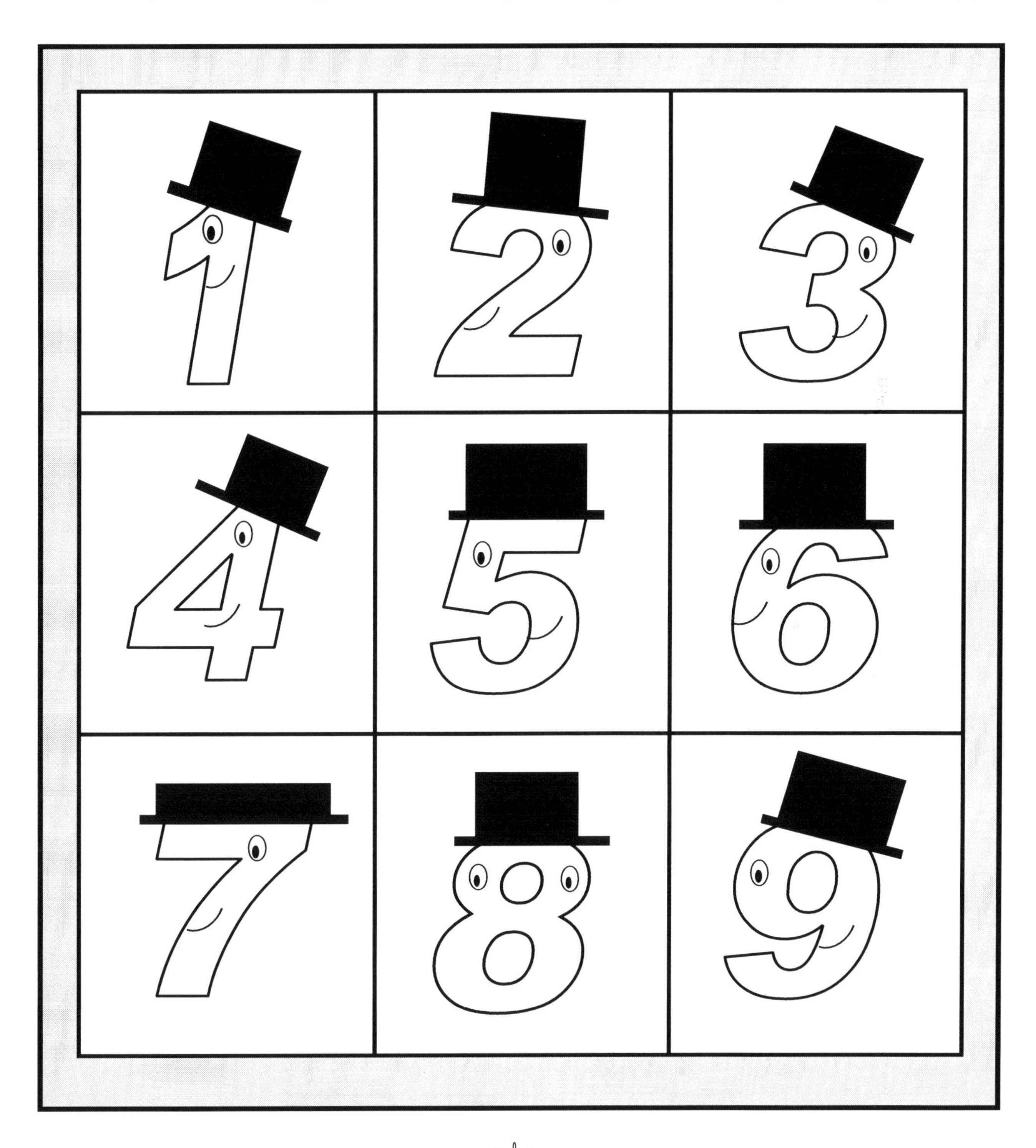

1	2	3	4	5	6	7	8	9
un	deux	trois	quatre	cinq	six	sept	huit	neuf

Can I say 10 numbers in French? jaune

Start at "**Départ**", roll the dice and count that number of spaces.
Say the number you land on in French. To win, arrive first at "Arrivée."

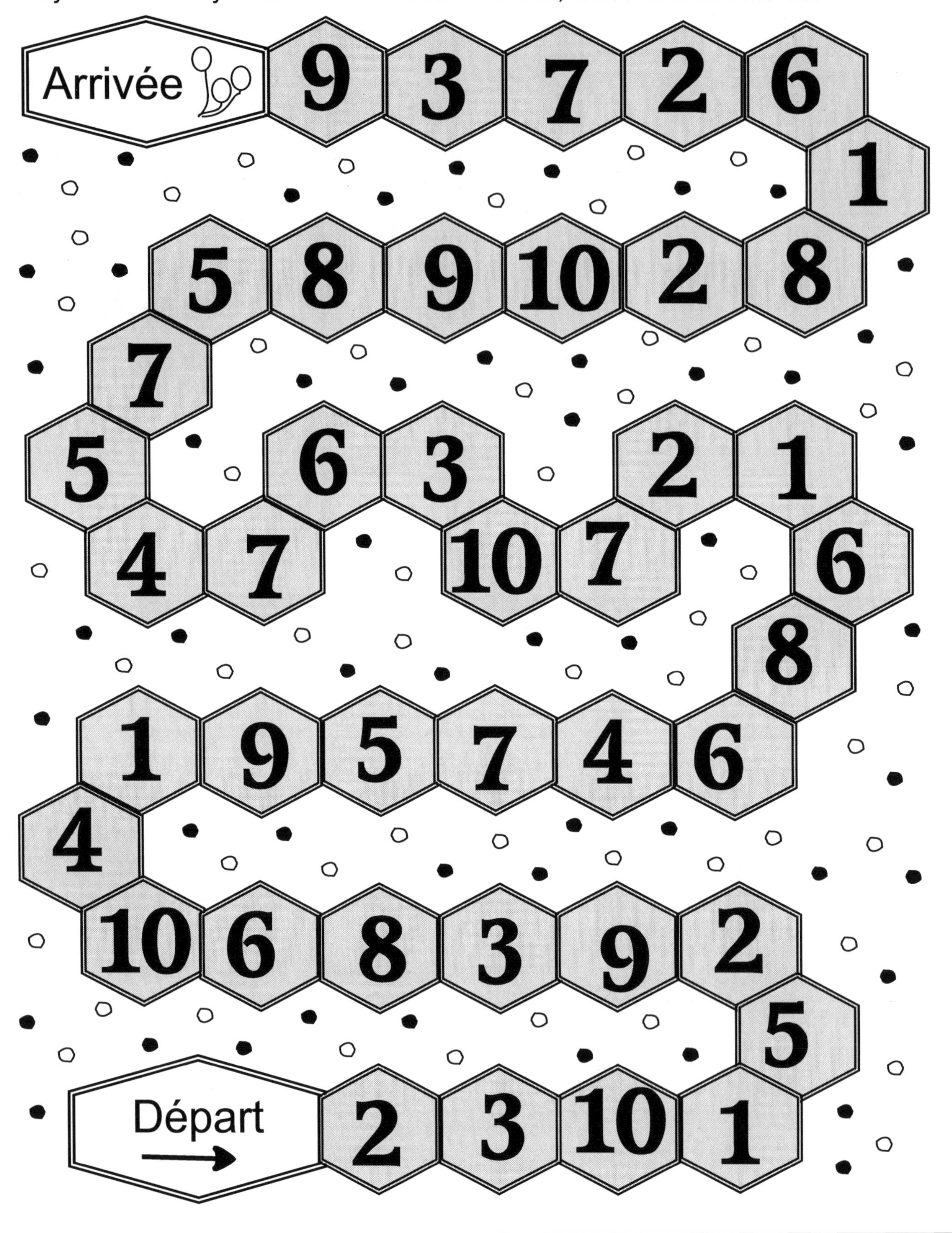

1	2	3	4	5	6	7	8	9	10
un	deux	trois	quatre	cinq	six	sept	huit	neuf	dix

Can I say 12 numbers in French?

Start at “Départ”, roll the dice and count that number of squares. If the final square has the bottom of the ladder in it go up it, or if it has the head of a snake go down it. Say the number of the square you land on in French. Take turns to roll the dice. To win, arrive first at "Arrivée."

1	2	3	4	5	6	7	8	9	10	11	12
un	deux	trois	quatre	cinq	six	sept	huit	neuf	dix	onze	douze

Can I say 12 numbers in French?

Each person / team needs 5 coloured counters or cubes of one colour (or a set of noughts or a set of crosses).

Say the French word for the number as you cover it with your counter. To win you have to get 3 in a row (vertically, horizontally or diagonally).

1	2	3
4	5	6
7	8	9
10	11	12

1	2	3	4	5	6	7	8	9	10	11	12
un	deux	trois	quatre	cinq	six	sept	huit	neuf	dix	onze	douze

Teachers note: Ask the pupils to match the picture mini card to the correct word card.
See page 75 for pair work activities using the mini cards, and page 77 for class activities.

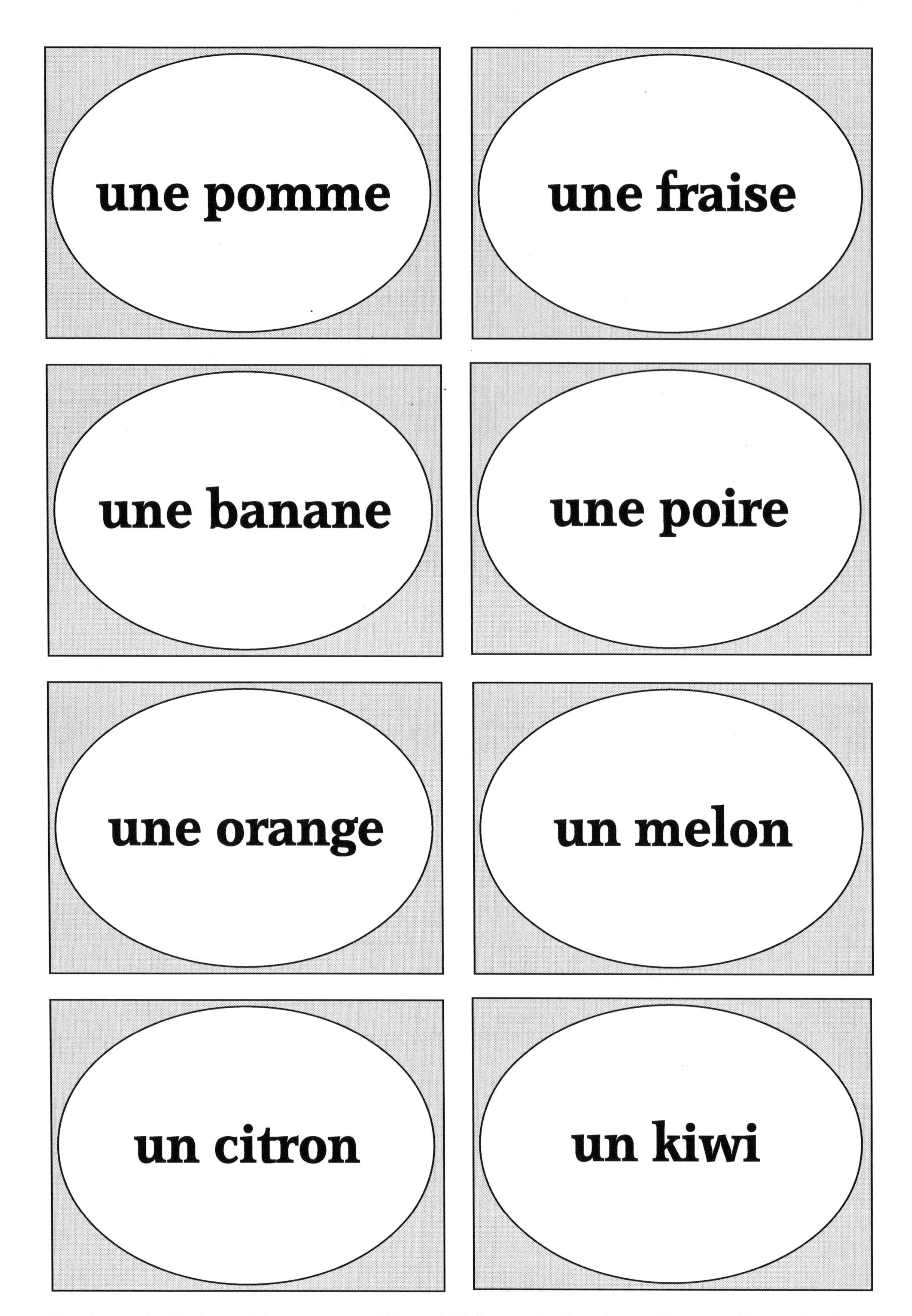

Teachers note: Photocopy this page (on card if possible), then make 8 cards by cutting round the cards. If you use card of **3 or 4 different colours** it is easier to separate the sets when handing them out to the class.

Can I say 4 fruits & 1 to 5 in French?

Each person / team needs 5 coloured counters or cubes of one colour (or a set of noughts or a set of crosses). Say the French word for the fruit or number as you place your counter on it. To win you have to get 3 in a row (vertically, horizontally or diagonally).

1 = un 2 = deux 3 = trois 4 = quatre 5 = cinq

une orange

une banane

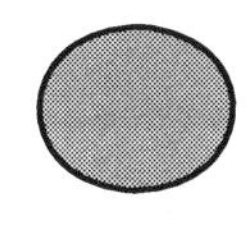

un kiwi

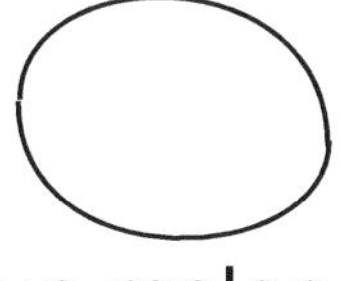

un melon

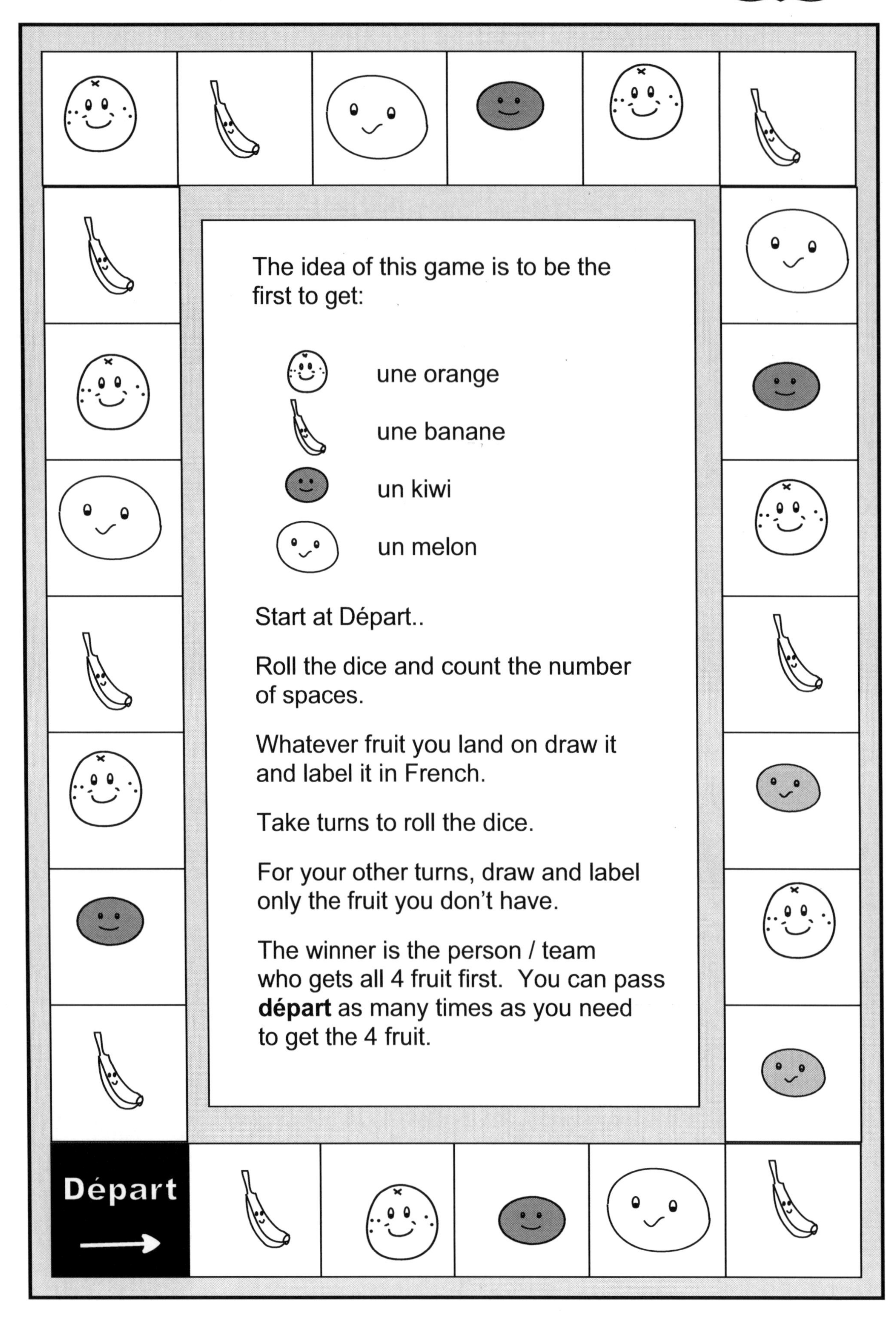
The idea of this game is to be the first to get:
une orange
une banane
un kiwi
un melon
Start at Départ..
Roll the dice and count the number of spaces.
Whatever fruit you land on draw it and label it in French.
Take turns to roll the dice.
For your other turns, draw and label only the fruit you don't have.
The winner is the person / team who gets all 4 fruit first. You can pass **départ** as many times as you need to get the 4 fruit.
Départ

Can I say 6 fruits in French?

Each person / team needs 5 coloured counters or cubes of one colour (or a set of noughts or a set of crosses).
Say the French word for the fruit or number as you place your counter.
To win you have to get 3 in a row (vertically, horizontally or diagonally).

8 = huit

     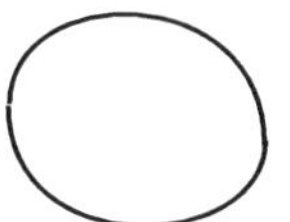

une orange   une banane   une pomme   une fraise   un kiwi   un melon

Can I say 6 fruits in French?

Start at "Départ", roll the dice and count that number of squares. If the final square has the bottom of the ladder in it go up it, or if it has the head of a snake go down it. Say the fruit you land on in French. Take turns to roll the dice. To win, arrive first at "Arrivée."

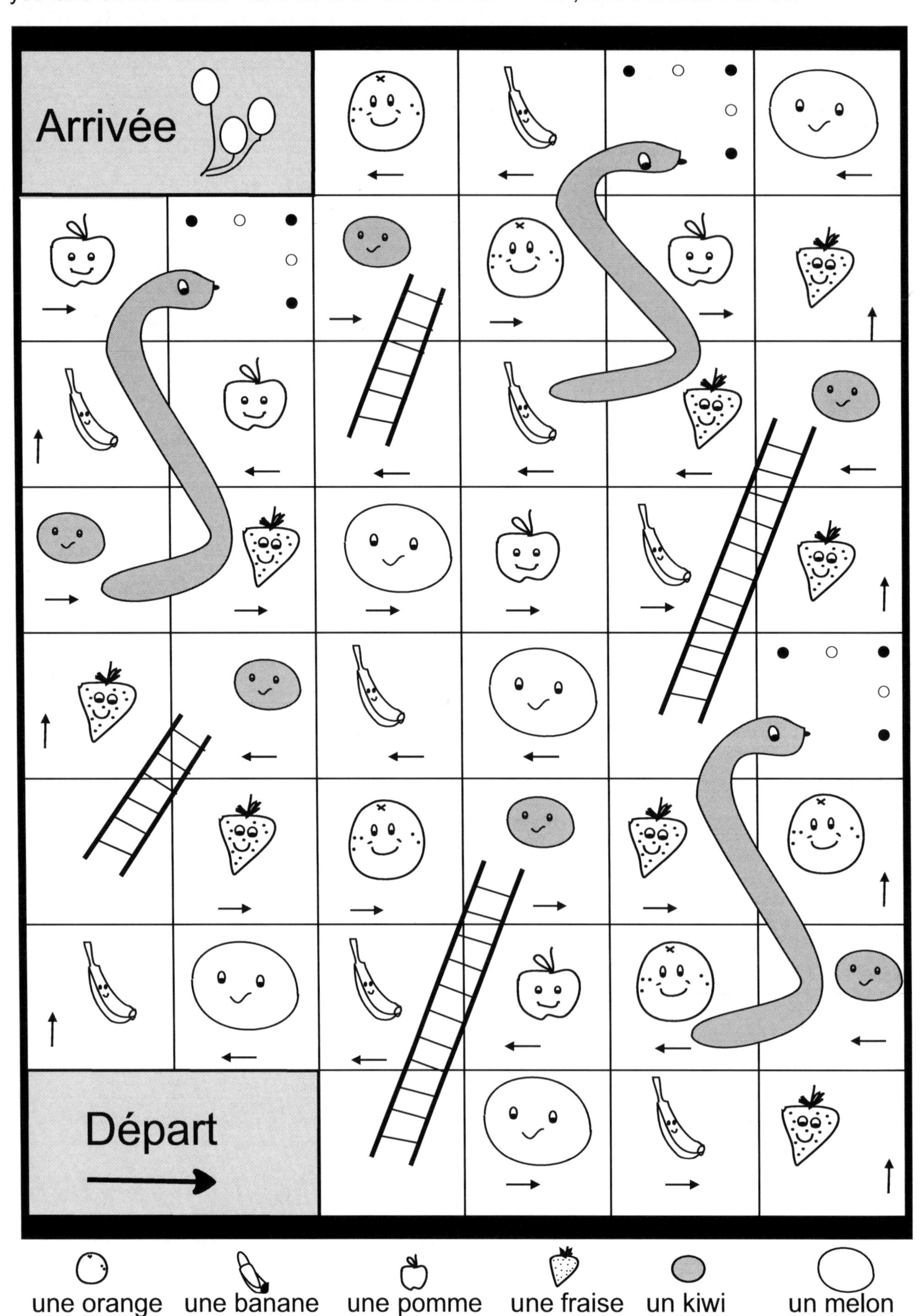

une orange une banane une pomme une fraise un kiwi un melon

Can I say 9 fruits in French?

Each person / team needs 5 coloured counters or cubes of one colour (or a set of noughts or a set of crosses).
Say the French word for the fruit as you cover it with your counter.
To win you have to get 3 in a row (vertically, horizontally or diagonally).

une banane = a banana   une poire = a pear   des cerises = some cherries

une pomme = an apple   une fraise = a strawberry   une orange = an orange

un kiwi = a kiwi   un citron = a lemon   un melon = a melon

Can I say 9 fruits in French?

Start at "**Départ**", roll the dice and count that number of spaces.
Say the fruit you land on in French. To win, arrive first at "Arrivée."

une banane = a banana une poire = a pear des cerises = some cherries

une pomme = an apple une fraise = a strawberry une orange = an orange

un kiwi = a kiwi un citron = a lemon un melon = a melon

Making sentences with fruit

When the pupils play the games, they could either practise just the vocabulary for the topic, or they could say a whole sentence. Here are some ideas of the sentences you could instruct a group, or the whole class to practise for the fruit topic:

1) **Asking if someone has a particular fruit**: Pupils could use either **Tu as.......?** (Do you have....? familiar form) or **Avez-vous.....?** (Do you have......? polite form) e.g. Tu as une pomme? Avez-vous une orange?

2) **Saying if you have a fruit**: **J'ai** (I have) e.g. J'ai une poire.

3) **Asking for a piece of fruit**: **Je voudrais .... s'il vous plaît** (I would like a __ please) e.g. Je voudrais une banane, s'il vous plaît.
Or say the fruit and then s'il vous plaît after it e.g. Une orange, s'il vous plaît.

3) **Saying what you are eating**: **Je mange** (I am eating) e.g. Je mange une fraise.

4) **Saying what you eat / are eating at lunchtime**: **À midi je mange** ....
(at lunchtime I eat / I am eating....) e.g. À midi je mange une pomme.

5) **Saying what colour the fruit are**: e.g. Une fraise, **c'est** rouge. (A strawberry, it's red) Une pomme, **c'est** rouge **ou** vert. (An apple, it's red or green)

6) **Using the correct word order for colours and nouns**: explain to the pupils that colours go after nouns in French and that some colours have extra letters added at the end of the words when the nouns are feminine or plural.
E.g. Vert changes to **verte** after une pomme and une poire e.g. une pomme verte.
And as cherries are plural rouge changes to **rouges**: des cerises rouges.
(une fraise rouge, une banane jaune, une orange orange, un melon jaune, un citron jaune, une pomme verte, une pomme rouge, une poire verte, des cerises rouges.)

7) **Asking what fruit friends like**. Tu aimes les..........? (Do you like.......?)
e.g. Tu aimes les fraises?

8) **Giving opinions or preferences about fruit.** In the word list section the fruit also appear in the plural form. This list can be photocopied and given to the pupils for when they are talking about which fruit they like.

J'aime = I like e.g. J'aime les oranges.

Je n'aime pas = I don't like e.g. Je n'aime pas les bananes.

J'adore = I love e.g. J'adore les fraises.

Je déteste = I hate e.g. Je déteste les cerises .

Je préfère = I prefer e.g. Je préfère les kiwis

9) **Going to the market:** Un kilo de .... s'il vous plaît (A kilo of ..... please)
Tell the pupils that if they went shopping they would usually ask for the fruit as a weight in kilos. After **un kilo de** you need to say the fruit in the plural, but without the word les (the), e.g. **Un kilo de fraises, s'il vous plaît**. Also, tell the pupils that it would be **Un kilo d'oranges** as oranges start with a vowel.

Teachers note: You could ask the pupils to match the picture mini card to the correct word card. See page 75 for pair work activities using the mini cards, and page 77 for class activities.

Teachers note: Photocopy this page (on card if possible), then make 8 cards by cutting round the cards. If you use card of **3 or 4 different colours** it is easier to separate the sets when handing them out to the class.

Can I say 4 drinks in French?

vert

Start at **départ**, roll the dice and count that number of squares.
Say the drink you land on in French. To win, arrive first at **arrivée**.

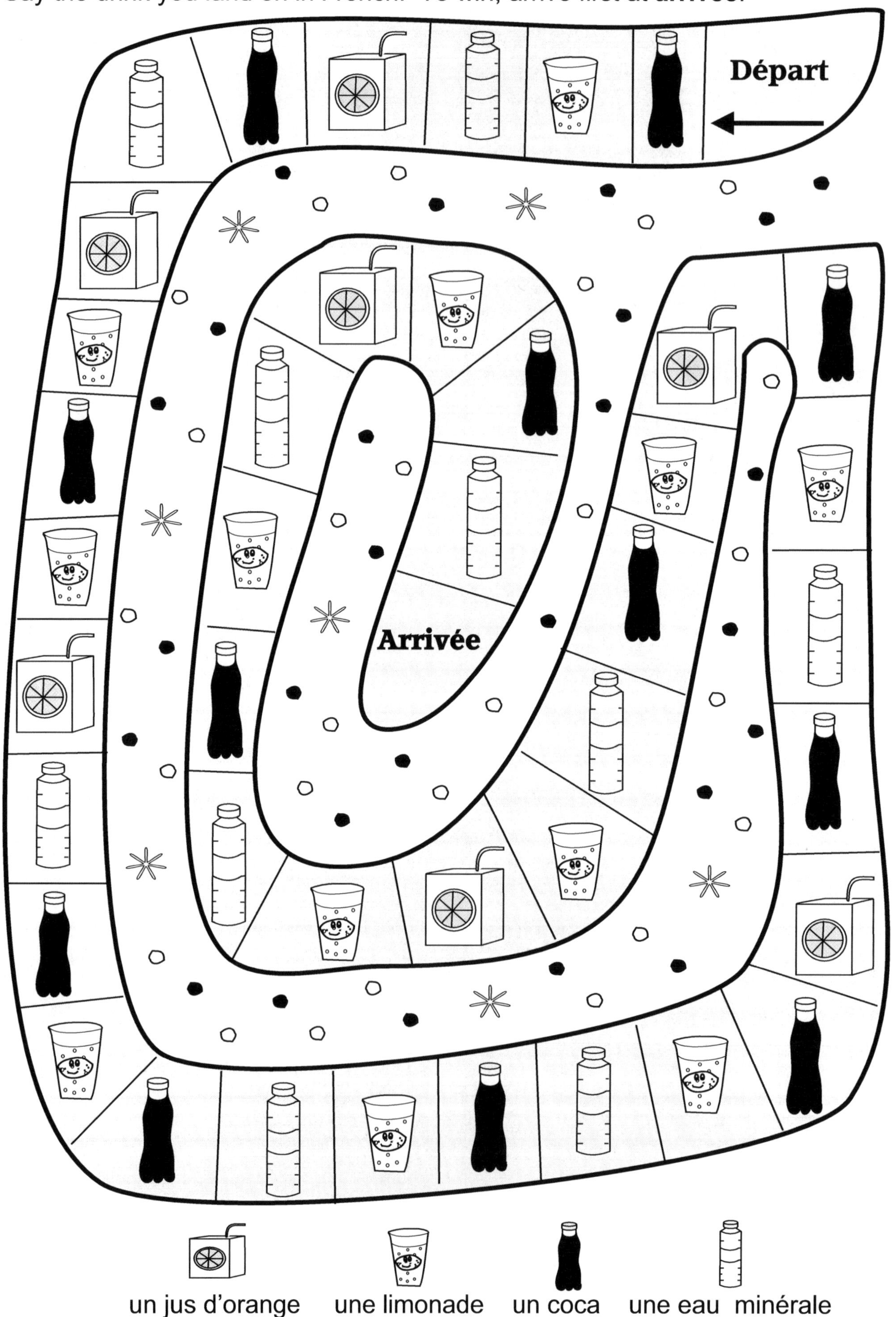

Can I say 4 drinks in French?

For this game, each person will need 8 domino cards. To make eight domino cards, with an adult cut along the dotted lines. Then, take turns to put a card down by matching a word to a picture or vice versa. If you cannot match a card, miss a turn. The winner is the person to either use all their cards, or use as many cards as possible.

Can I say 6 drinks in French?

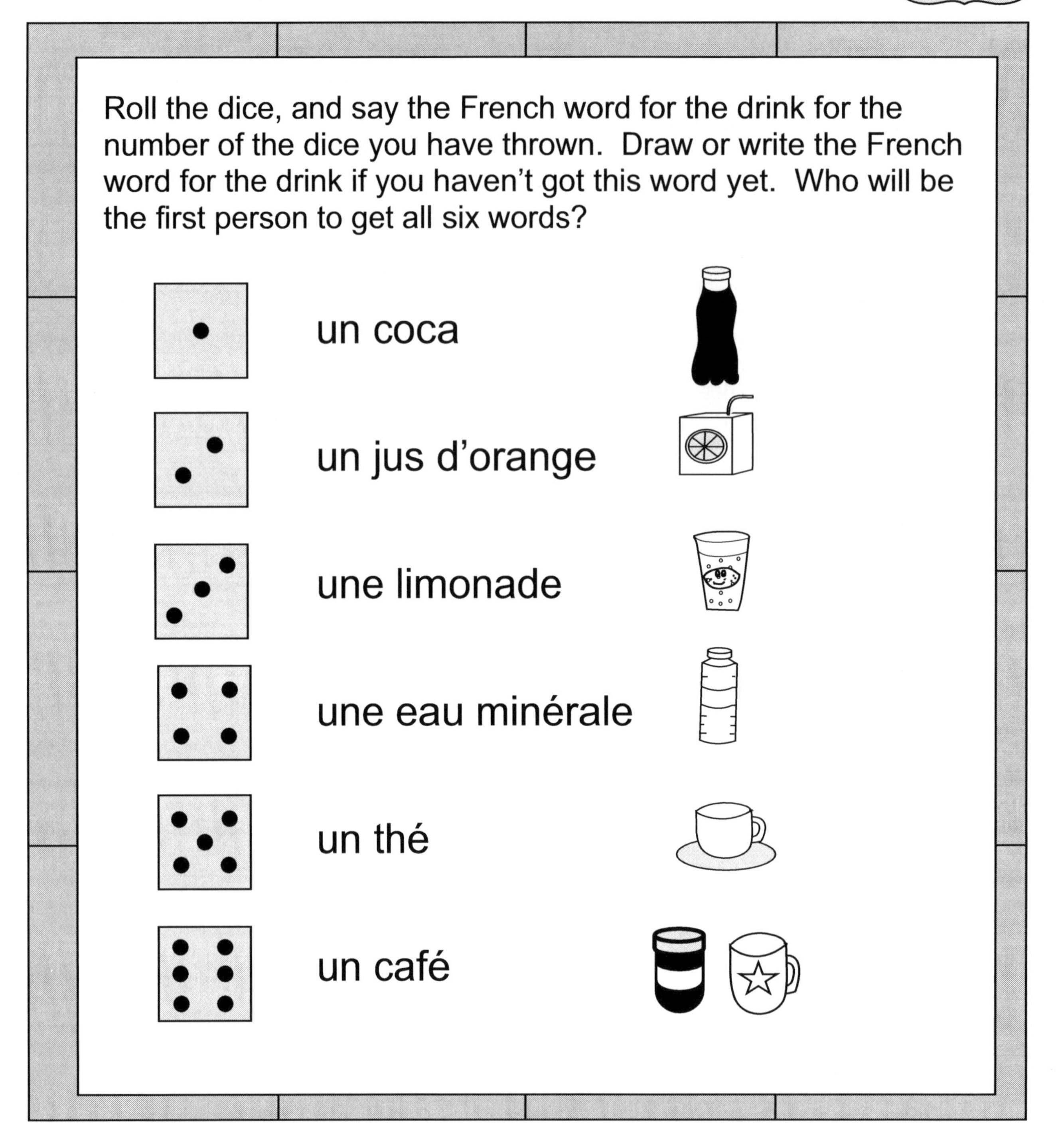

Guess the drink

In pairs, choose a drink and write it down so that your partner can't see it.

Take turns to guess each other's drink. Whoever guesses correctly the drink wins a point. Choose a new drink each, and write it down. Take turns to guess each other's drink.

Can I say 8 drinks in French?

Start at départ, roll the dice and count that number of squares.
Say the drink you land on in French. To win, arrive first at arrivée.

un jus d'orange un coca une limonade une eau minérale
un jus de pomme un coca light un thé un café

Can I say 8 drinks in French?

1 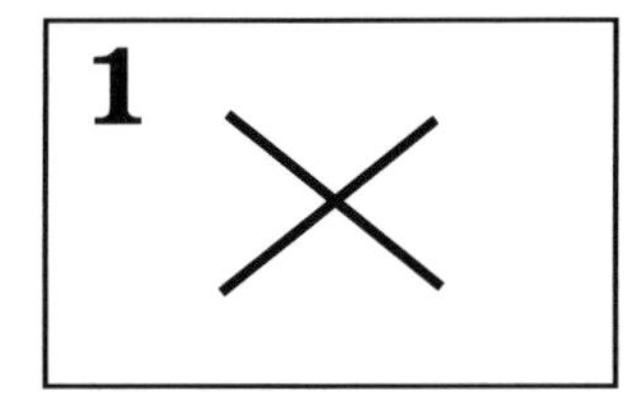	2  un jus d'orange	3 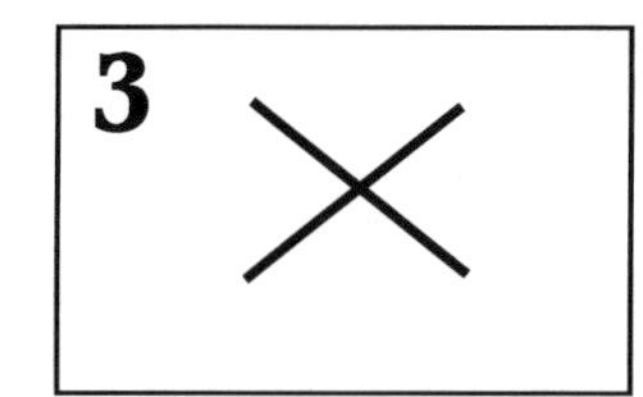	4  une limonade
5  une eau minérale	6 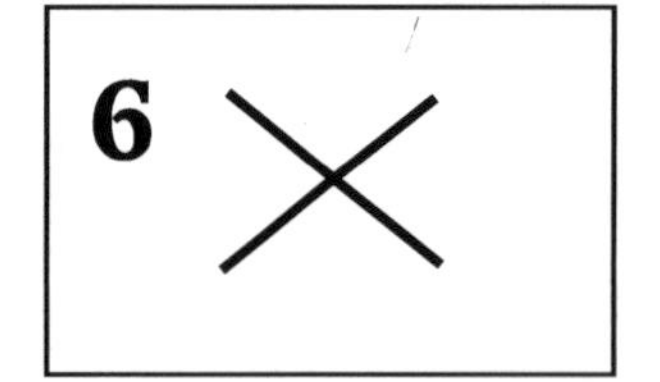	7  un jus de pomme	8  un café
9  un coca light	10  un thé	11 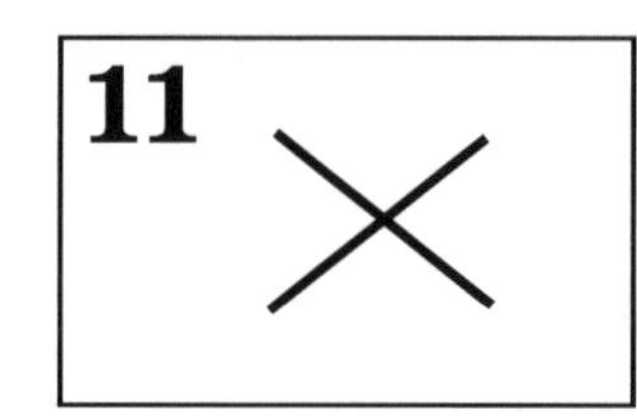	12  un coca

Roll two dice, and add the numbers together. Look at the above numbers, if there is a drink for the number you get, say what the drink is and win a point. Water is healthy, so if you get water you win two points! Who will be the first to ten points?

Making sentences with drinks

When the pupils play the games, they could either practise just the vocabulary for the topic, or they could say a whole sentence. Here are some ideas of the sentences you could instruct a group, or the whole class to practise for the drinks topic:

1) **Asking for a drink: Je voudrais ...... s'il vous plaît** (I would like ....please)
e.g Je voudrais un jus d'orange, s'il vous plaît
Or say the drink, and then s'il vous plaît after it e.g. un jus d'orange, s'il vous plaît

2) **Saying what you are drinking**: Je bois (I am drinking) e.g. Je bois un coca.

3) **Giving opinions or preferences about drinks:**

J'aime = I like   Je n'aime pas = I don't like   Je préfère = I prefer

Tell the pupils that when they say what drinks they like, dislike or prefer they need to use either le or la (the) instead of the un or une (a).

4) **Asking if there are certain drinks** Avez-vous......? (Do you have....?)
e.g. Avez-vous un coca light?

5) **Saying there isn't certain drinks** (as unfortunately sometimes cafés run out or may not sell what you want). Il n'y a pas de .... there isn't
After il n'y a pas de you omit the un / une that appears before the drinks
e.g. il n'y a pas de coca.

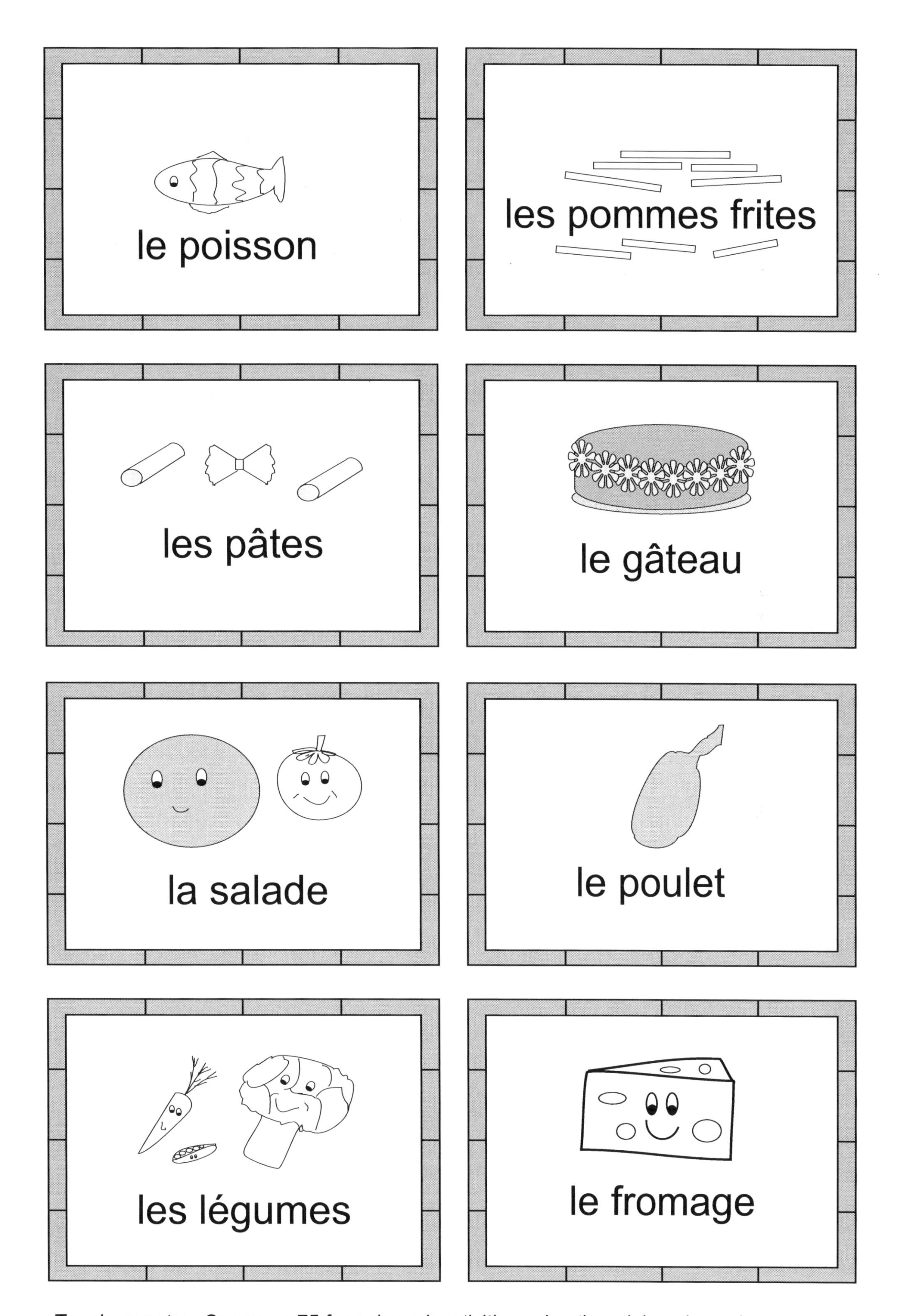

Teachers note: See page 75 for pair work activities using the mini cards, and page 77 for class activities.

Can I say 4 types of food in French?

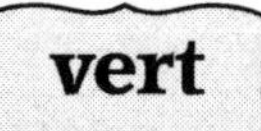

Start at **Départ**, roll the dice and count that number of spaces. Say the word for the space you land on in French. Take turns to roll the dice. To win, arrive first at **Arrivée.**

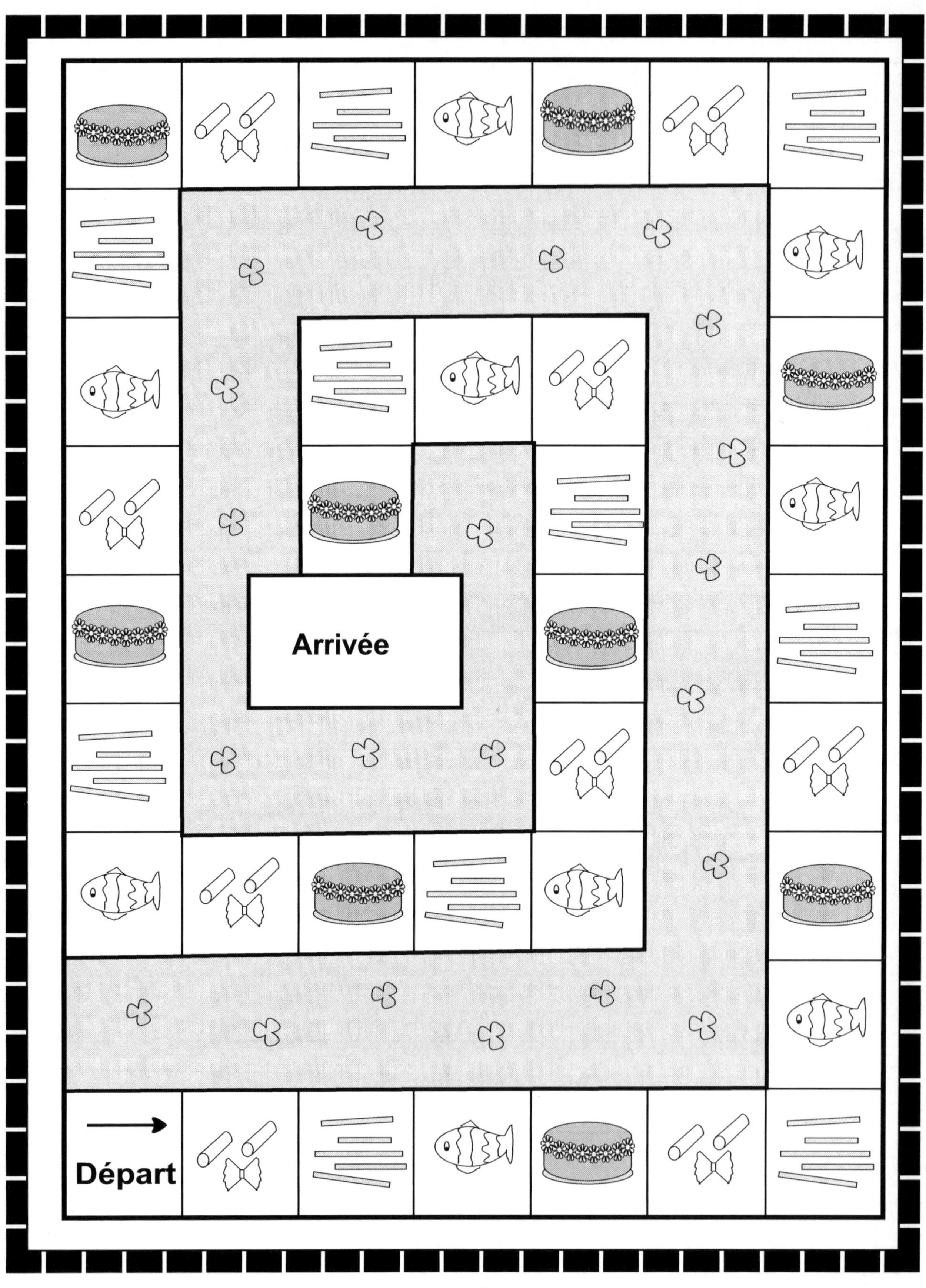

les pâtes

les pommes frites

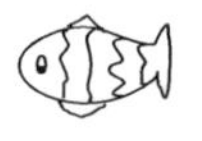

le poisson

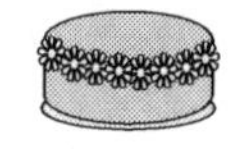

le gâteau

Can I say 4 types of food in French?

Each person / team needs 5 coloured counters or cubes of one colour (or a set of noughts or a set of crosses). Say the French word for the food item as you cover it with your counter. To win you have to get 4 in a row (vertically, horizontally or diagonally).

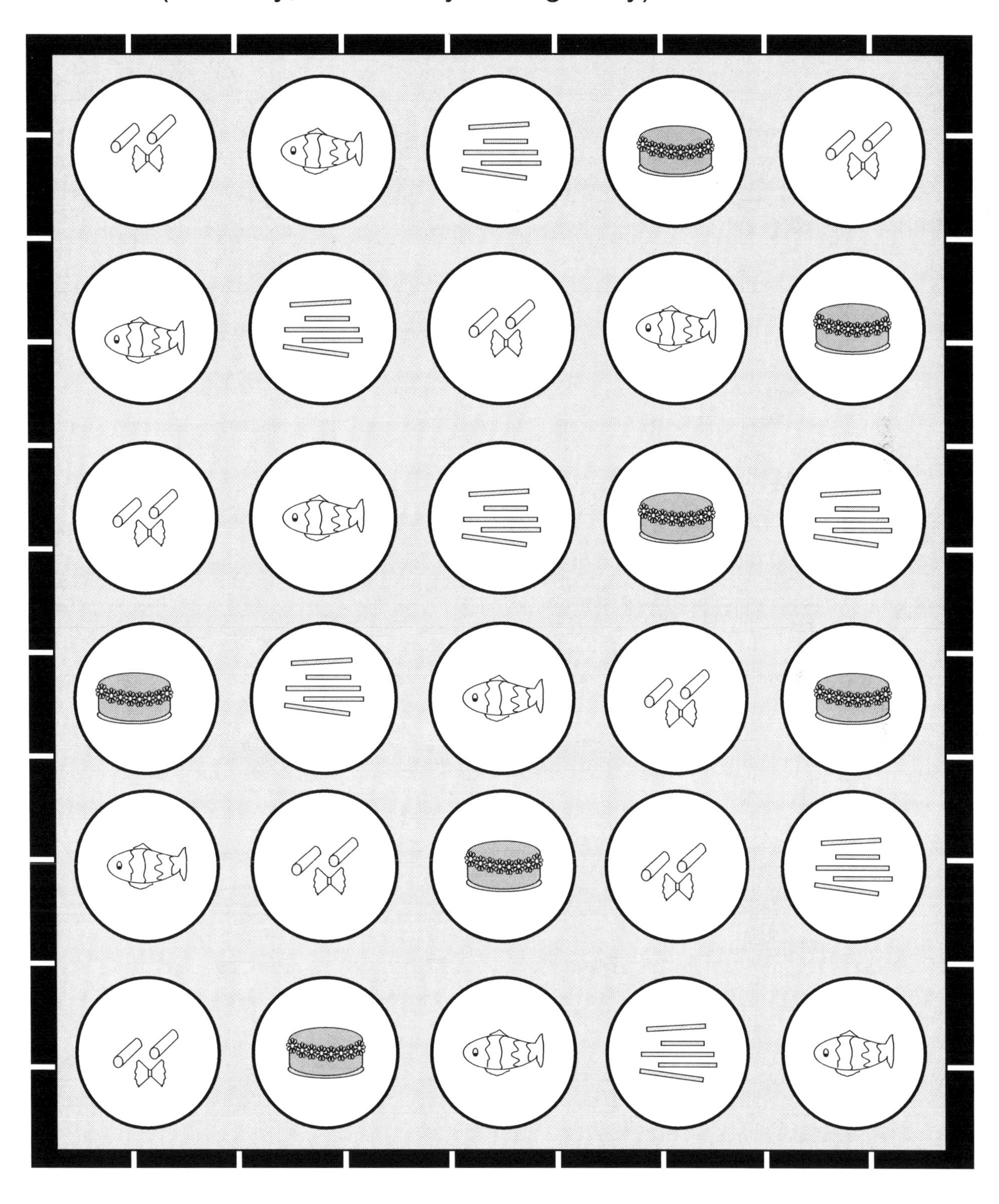

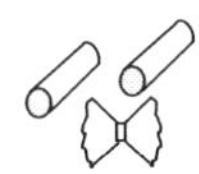

les pâtes

les pommes frites

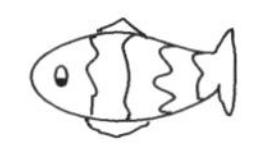

le poisson

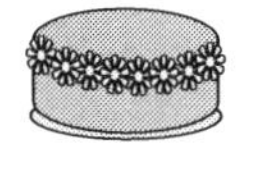

le gâteau

Can I say 6 types of food in French?

Start at "Départ", roll the dice and count that number of squares. If the final square has the bottom of the ladder in it go up it, or if it has the head of a snake go down it. Say the item of clothing you land on in French. Take turns to roll the dice. To win, arrive first at "Arrivée."

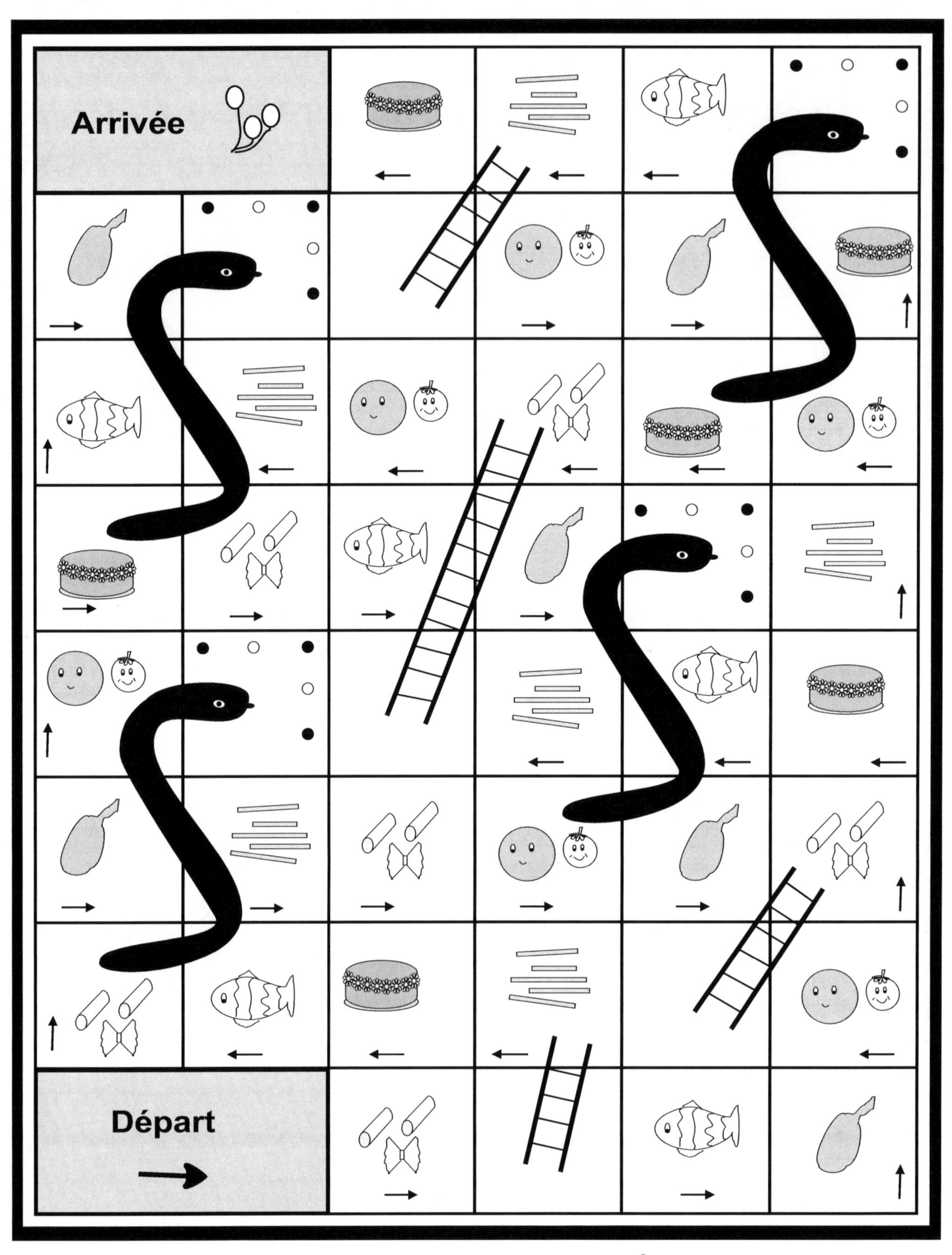

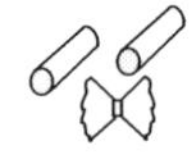
les pâtes

les pommes frites

le poisson

le poulet

la salade

le gâteau

Can I say 6 types of food in French?

For this game, each person will need 8 domino cards. To make eight domino cards, with an adult cut along the dotted lines. Then, take turns to put a card down by matching a word to a picture or vice versa. If you cannot match a card, miss a turn. The winner is the person to either use all their cards, or use as many cards as possible.

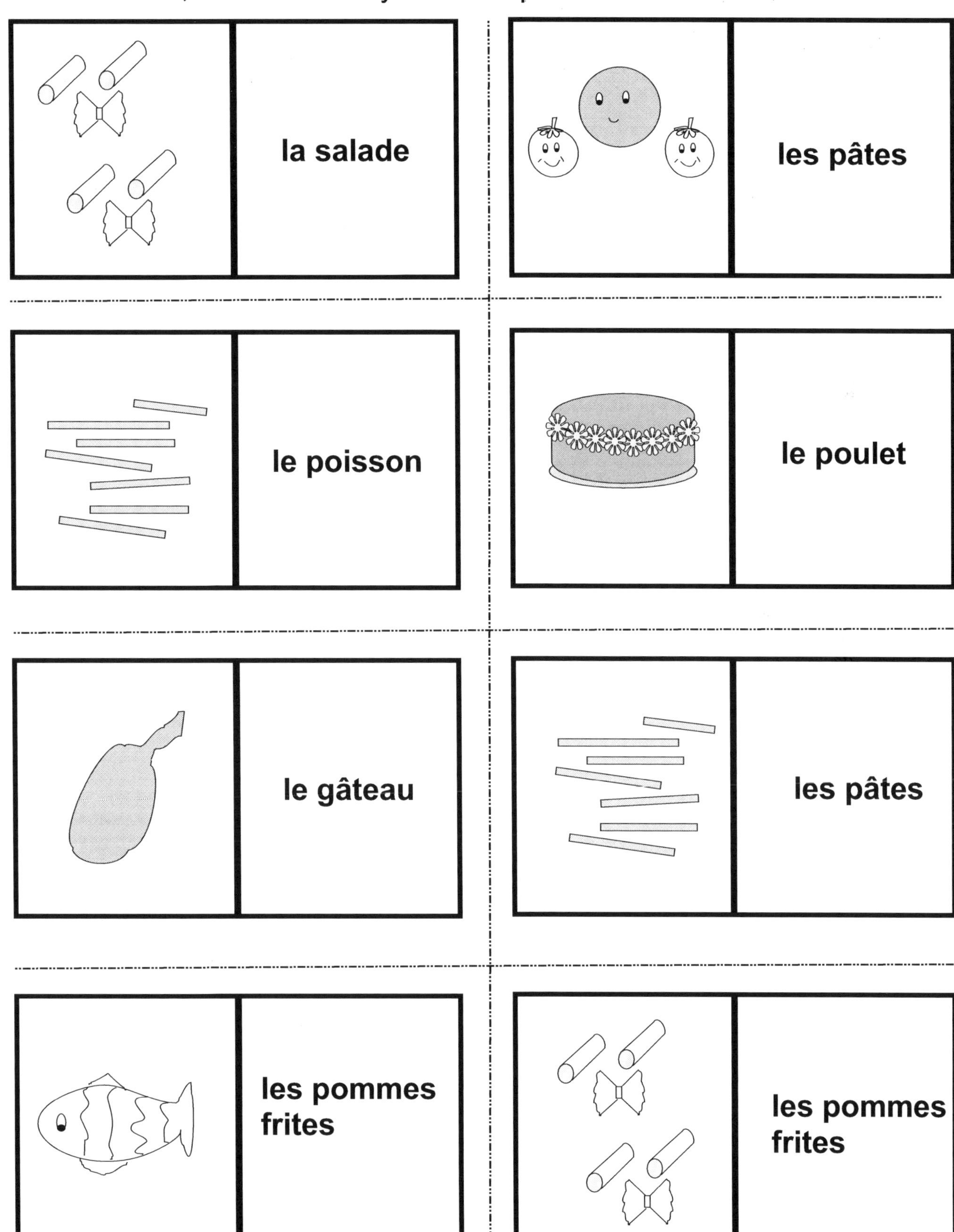

Can I say 8 types of food in French?

Start at "**Départ**", roll the dice and count that number of spaces. Say the word for the space you land on in French. Take turns to roll the dice. Each time you pass "départ" you get a point. Who will be the first person to get three points?

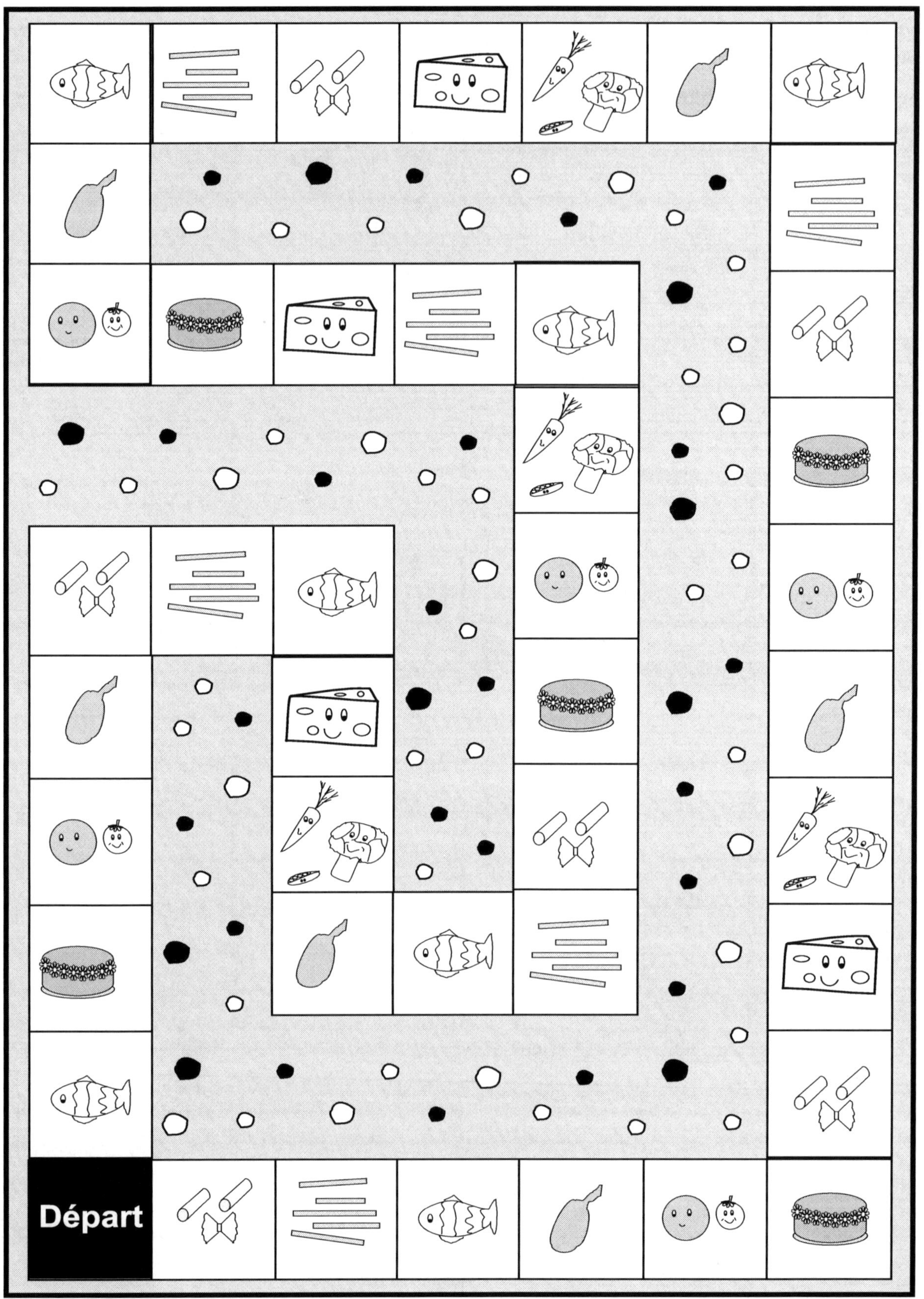

les pâtes | les pommes frites | le poisson | le poulet | le fromage | les légumes | la salade | le gâteau

Can I say 8 types of food in French?

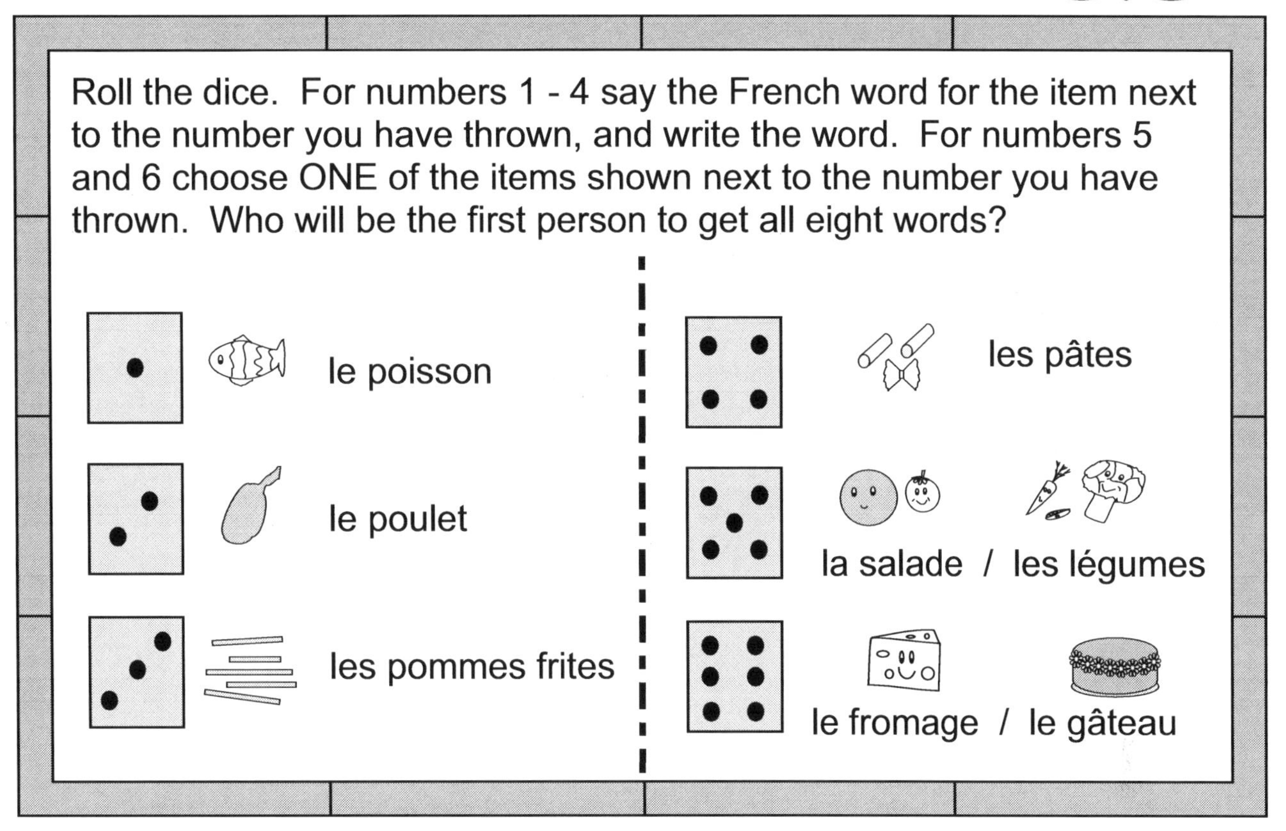

Making sentences with food

When the pupils play the games, they could either practise just the vocabulary for the topic, or they could say a whole sentence. Here are some ideas of the sentences you could instruct a group, or the whole class to practise for the food topic:

1) Pretending to order some food:

The pupils could say the food item then s'il vous plaît e.g. le poulet, s'il vous plaît.

The pupils could say Je voudrais, then a food item, then s'il vous plaît.
E.g. Je voudrais le poisson s'il vous plaît.

2) Giving opinions about food:
J'aime = I like   Je n'aime pas = I don't like   Je préfère = I prefer
E.g. J'aime les pommes frites. Je n'aime pas les légumes.

3) **Asking what food friends like:** Tu aimes ....? (Do you like.......?)
e.g. Tu aimes le poisson?

4) **Saying what you are eating**: Je mange (I am eating)
e.g. Je mange la salade

5) **Saying there isn't certain foods** (as unfortunately sometimes cafés run out of things). Il n'y a pas de .... there isn't   E.g. Il n'y a pas de poulet.
After il n'y a pas de you omit the le / la / les that appears before the food.

Teachers note: You could ask the pupils to match the picture mini card to the correct word card. See page 75 for pair work activities using the mini cards, and page 77 for class activities.

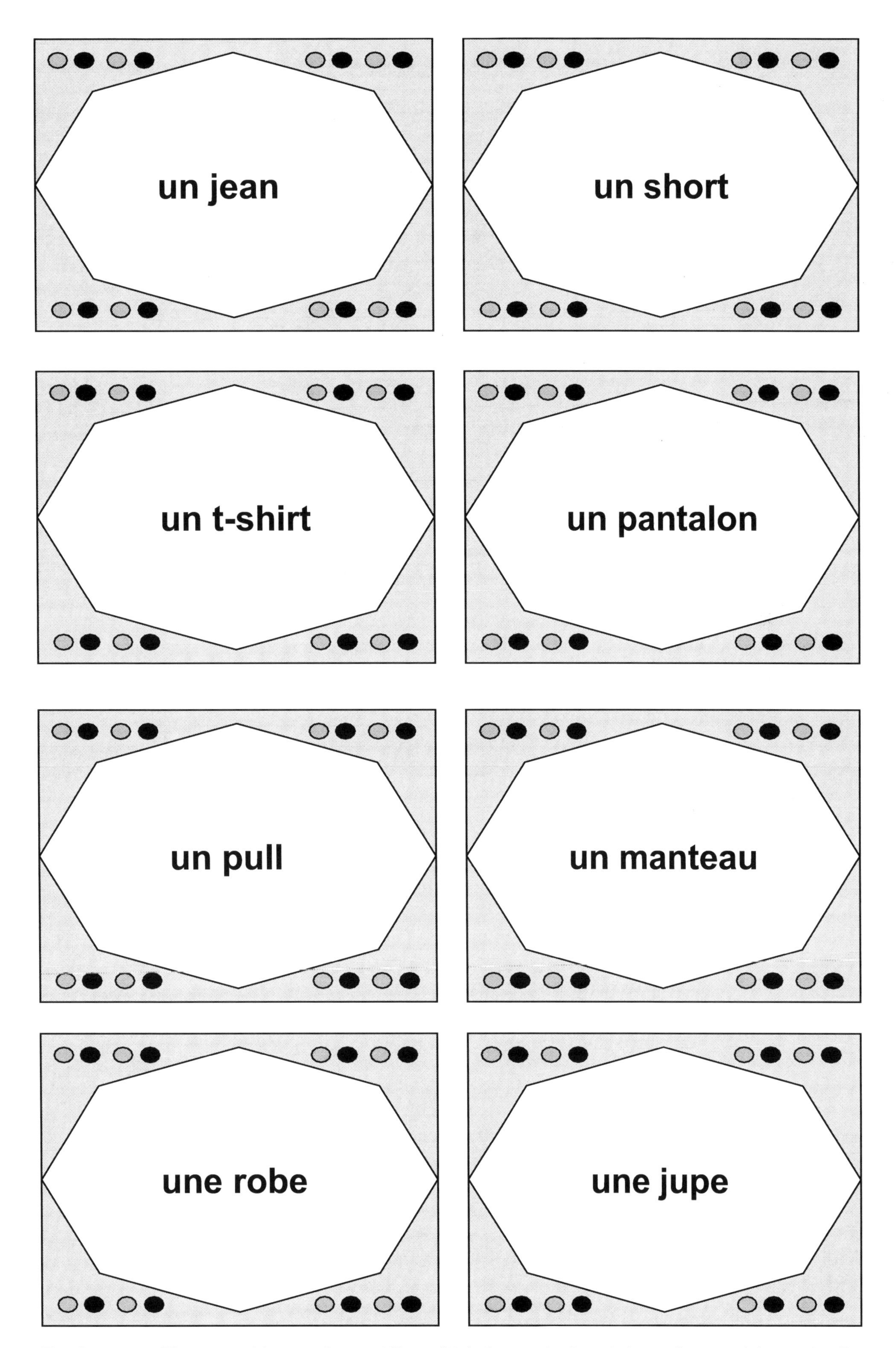

Teachers note: Photocopy this page (on card if possible), then make 8 cards by cutting round the cards. If you use card of **3 or 4 different colours** it is easier to separate the sets when handing them out to the class.

Can I say 4 items of clothing in French?

Start at "Départ", roll the dice and count that number of squares. If the final square has the bottom of the ladder in it go up it, or if it has the head of a snake go down it. Say the item of clothing you land on in French. Take turns to roll the dice. To win, arrive first at "Arrivée."

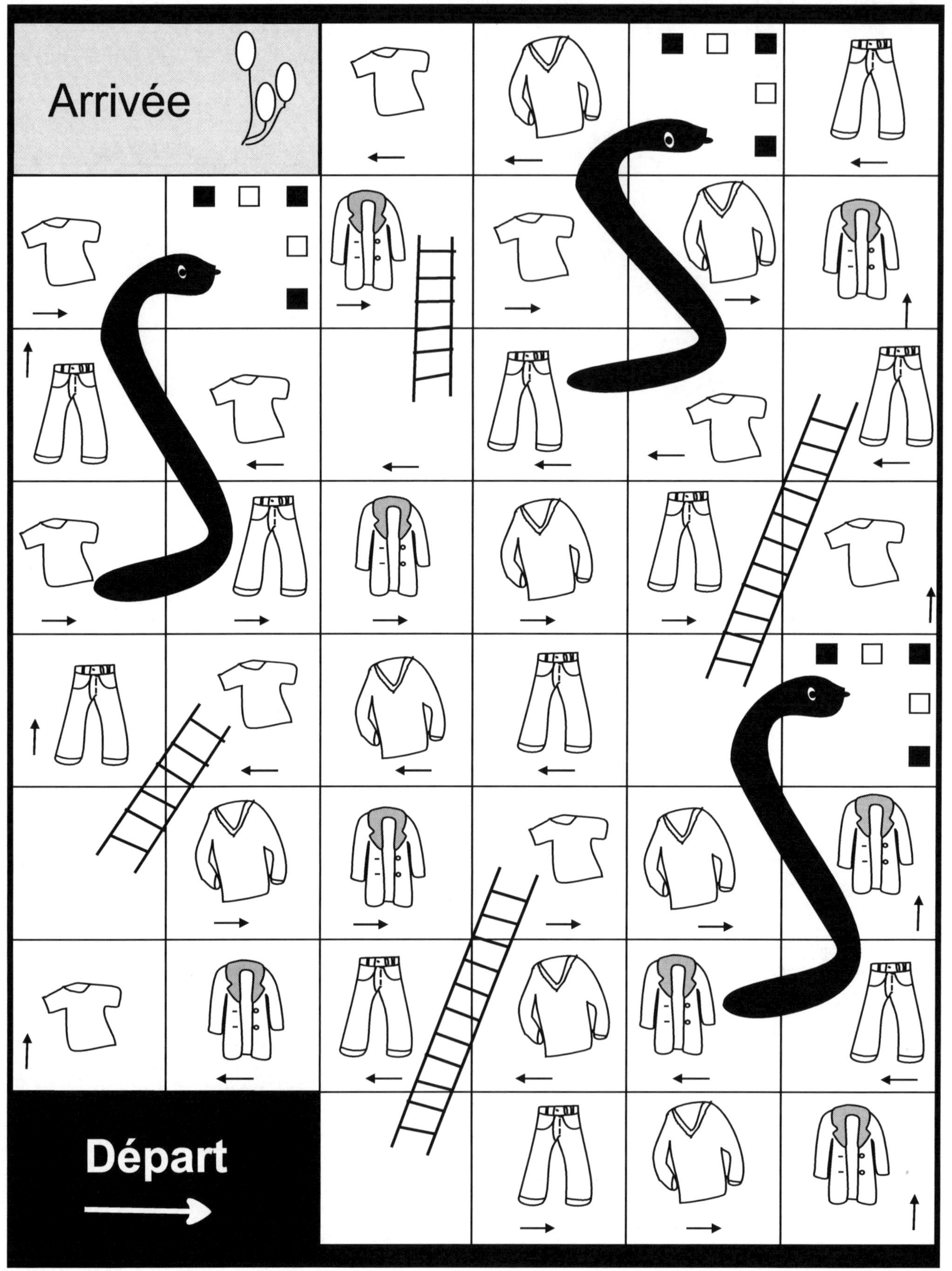

un t-shirt = a t-shirt un jean = jeans un pull= a jumper un manteau = a coat

Can I say 4 items of clothing in French?

For this game, each person will need 8 domino cards. To make eight domino cards, with an adult cut along the dotted lines. Then, take turns to put a card down by matching a word to a picture or vice versa. If you cannot match a card, miss a turn. The winner is the person to either use all their cards, or use as many cards as possible.

Can I say 6 items of clothing in French?

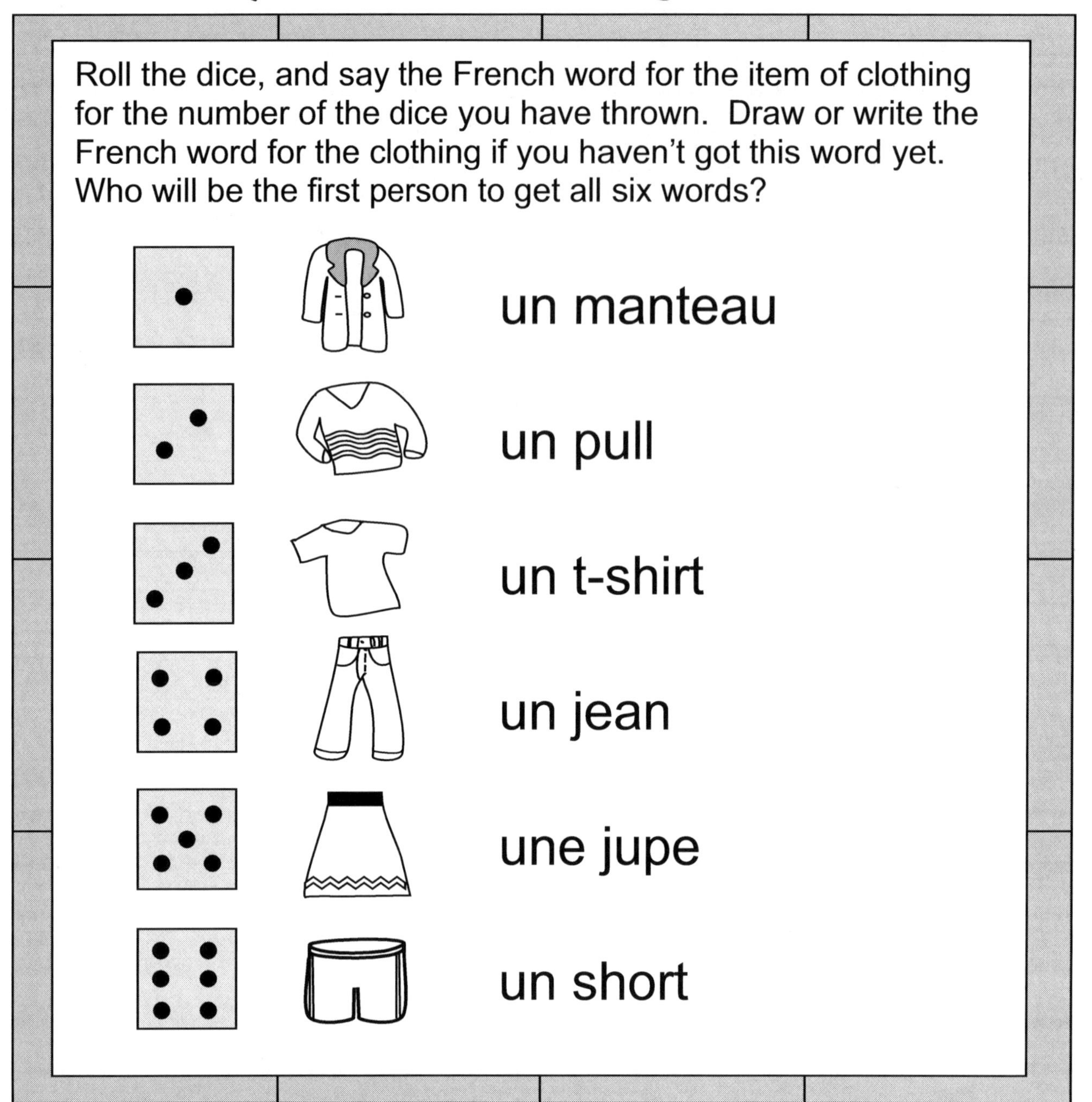

Guess the picture!

Take turns to draw on a mini whiteboard one of the above items of clothing, and the other person has to guess the word in French.

How many items of clothing can you remember?

Look at the words for the six items of clothing for about a minute, then turn over this page. In pairs, write down as many words as you can remember on a mini whiteboard. Finally, look again at the words and see how many you got right. Have a point for the correct spelling of a word and half a point if you misspelt one. How many points can you get?

Can I say 9 items of clothing? in French? rouge

Each person / team needs 24 coloured counters or cubes of one colour, or can use a pencil to draw noughts or crosses directly onto the sheet.
Say the French word for the item of clothing as you choose a space.
To win you have to get 4 in a row (vertically, horizontally or diagonally).

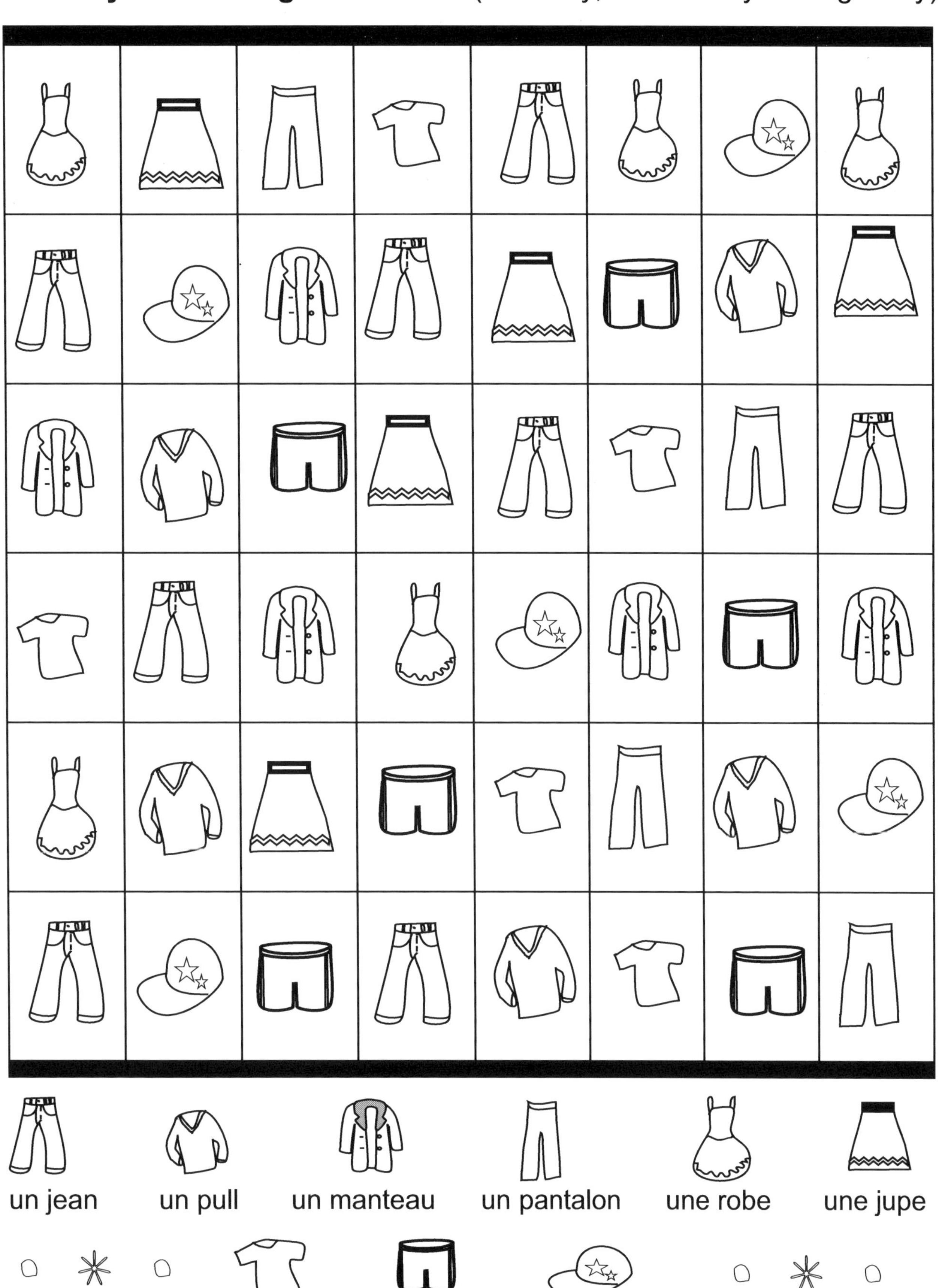

Can I say 9 items of clothing? in French?

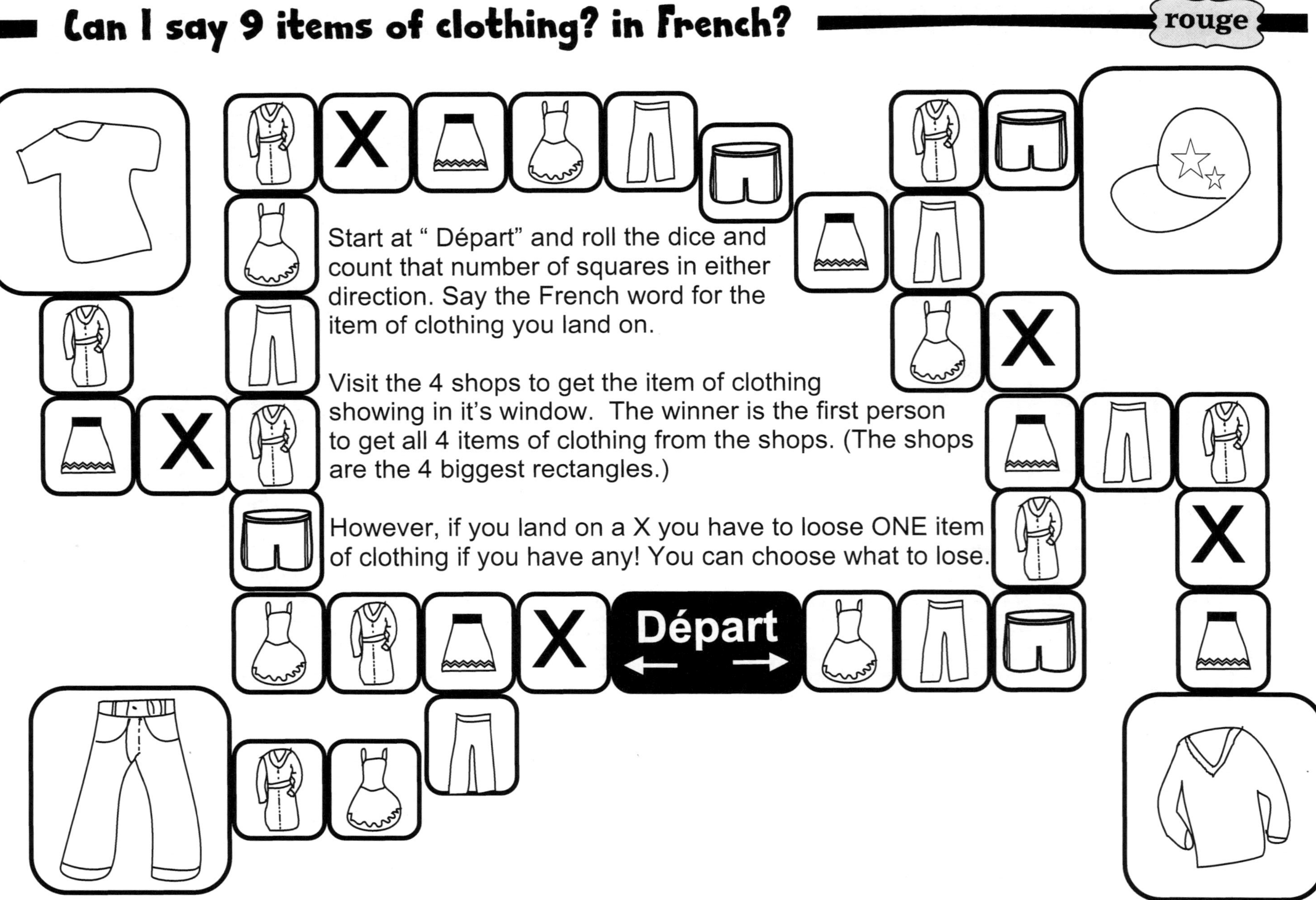

Making sentences with clothes

When the pupils play the games, they could either practise just the vocabulary for the topic, or they could say a whole sentence. Here are some ideas of the sentences you could instruct a group, or the whole class to practise for the clothes topic:

1) **Saying what you are wearing, or what he or she is wearing.**

je porte = I am wearing

il porte = he is wearing

elle porte = she is wearing

e.g. Je porte un t-shirt, il porte un jean, elle porte une robe.

This can be extended by starting the sentence with either **En été** (In summer) or **En hiver** (In winter) e.g. En hiver je porte un manteau.

2) **Asking a friend what they are wearing**:
Tu portes........? (Are you wearing ...?) e.g. Tu portes un manteau?

3) **Going shopping**: Pupils ask for the item by saying **Je voudrais ... s'il vous plaît** (I would like.....please) e.g. Je voudrais un pull, s'il vous plaît.

Or alternatively, just say the item of clothing, then add s'il vous plaît (please.) e.g. Une robe, s'il vous plaît.

4) **Describing the colour of the clothes**: Pupils invent a colour for the item of clothing, saying first the item of clothing then the colour. e.g. un pull vert.

Tell the pupils that in French the colours go after the noun.

Explain that for **feminine words** (une jupe, une robe, une casquette) the colour endings may change: e.g. une jupe verte. The colours change as follows

Some colours add an extra e: vert > **verte** bleu > **bleue** gris > **grise** noir > **noire**

Two colours add extra letters: violet > **violette** blanc > **blanche**

Some colours stay the same: rouge, orange, rose, jaune, marron

If you decide to not introduce the fact that some endings of colours change, you can instruct the pupils to decide if the item of clothing is either rouge, orange, rose, jaune or marron as these colours are the same for both the feminine and the masculine words when it is in the singular. The games can be coloured in by the pupils.

Teachers note: You could ask the pupils to match the picture mini card to the correct word card. See page 75 for pair work activities using the mini cards, and page 77 for class activities.

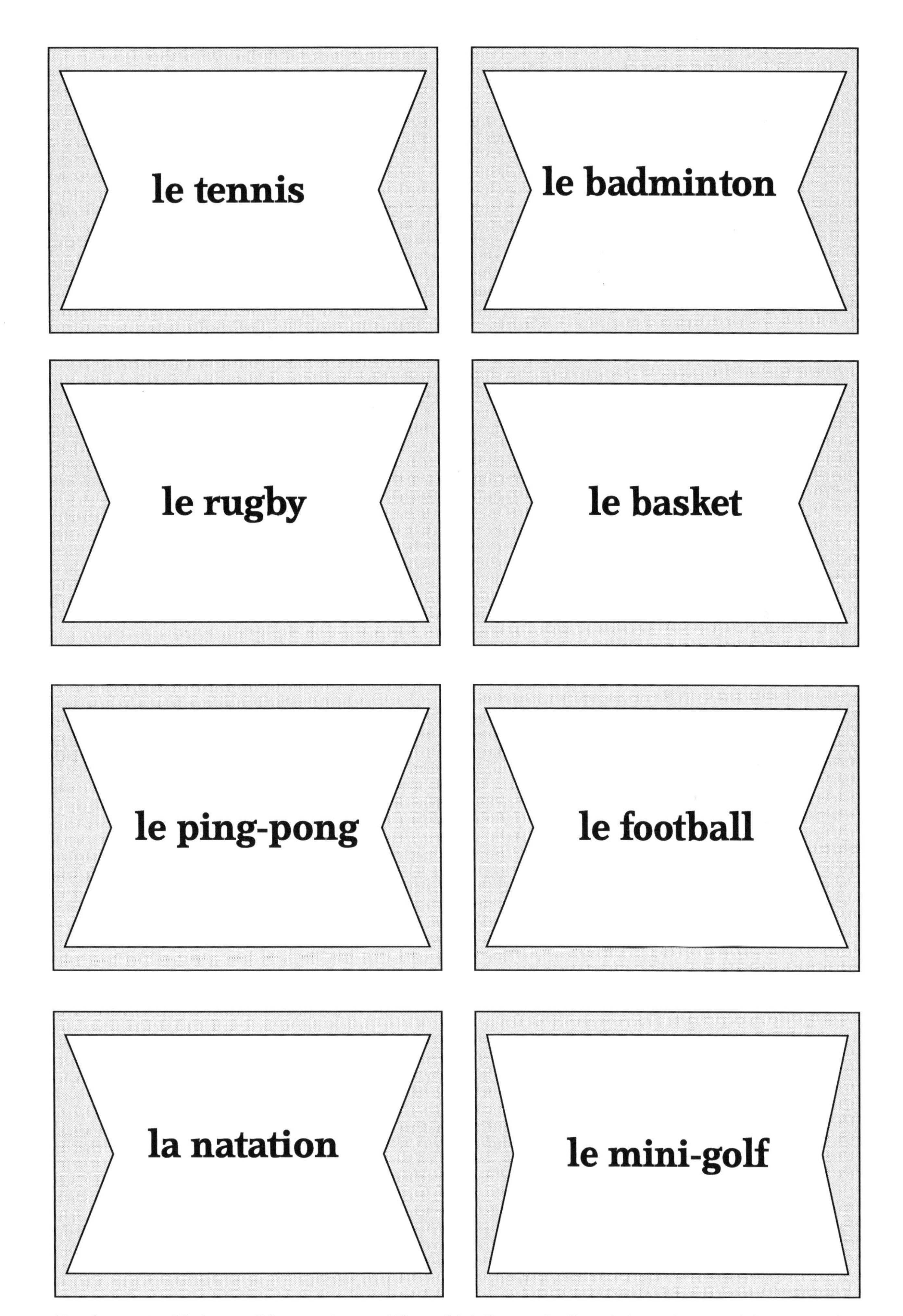

Teachers note: Photocopy this page (on card if possible), then make 8 cards by cutting round the cards. If you use card of **3 or 4 different colours** it is easier to separate the sets when handing them out to the class.

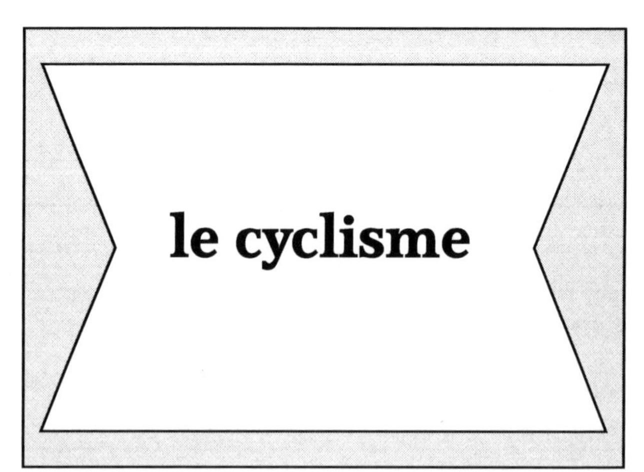
le cyclisme

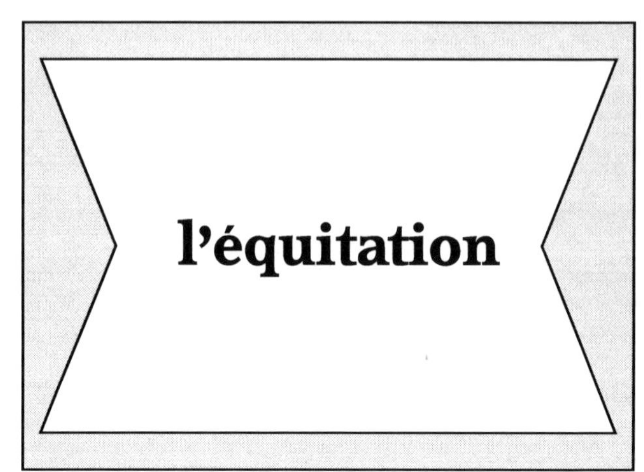
l’équitation

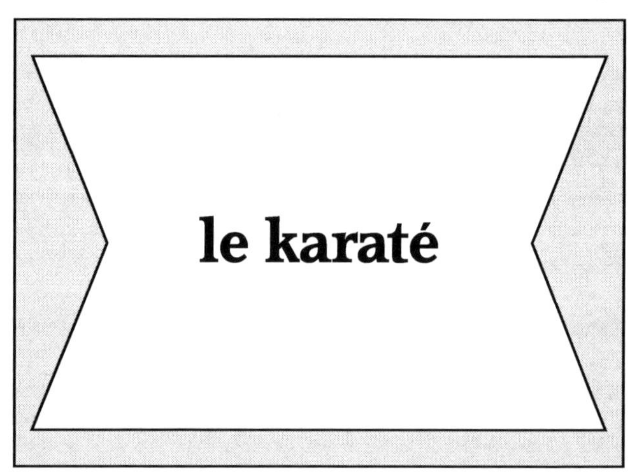
le karaté

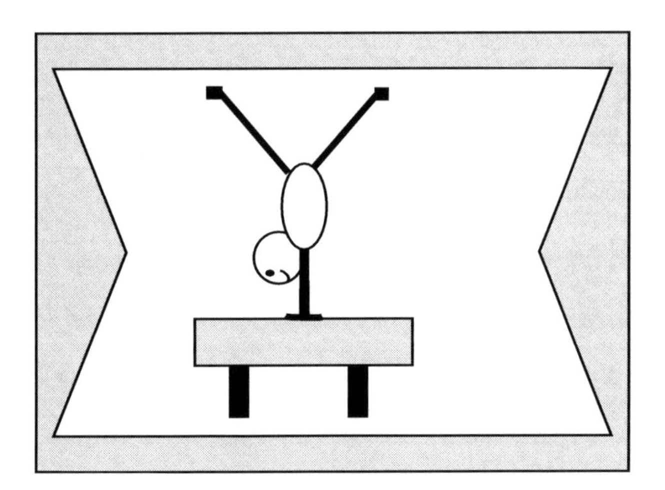

la gymnastique

Can I say 6 sports & some numbers?

Each person / team needs 5 coloured counters or cubes of one colour (or a set of noughts or a set of crosses). Say the French word for the sport or number as you place your counter. To win you have to get 3 in a row (vertically, horizontally or diagonally).

Can I say 6 sports in French?

vert

Start at "**Départ**", roll the dice and count that number of spaces.
Say the sport you land on in French. To win, arrive first at "Arrivée."

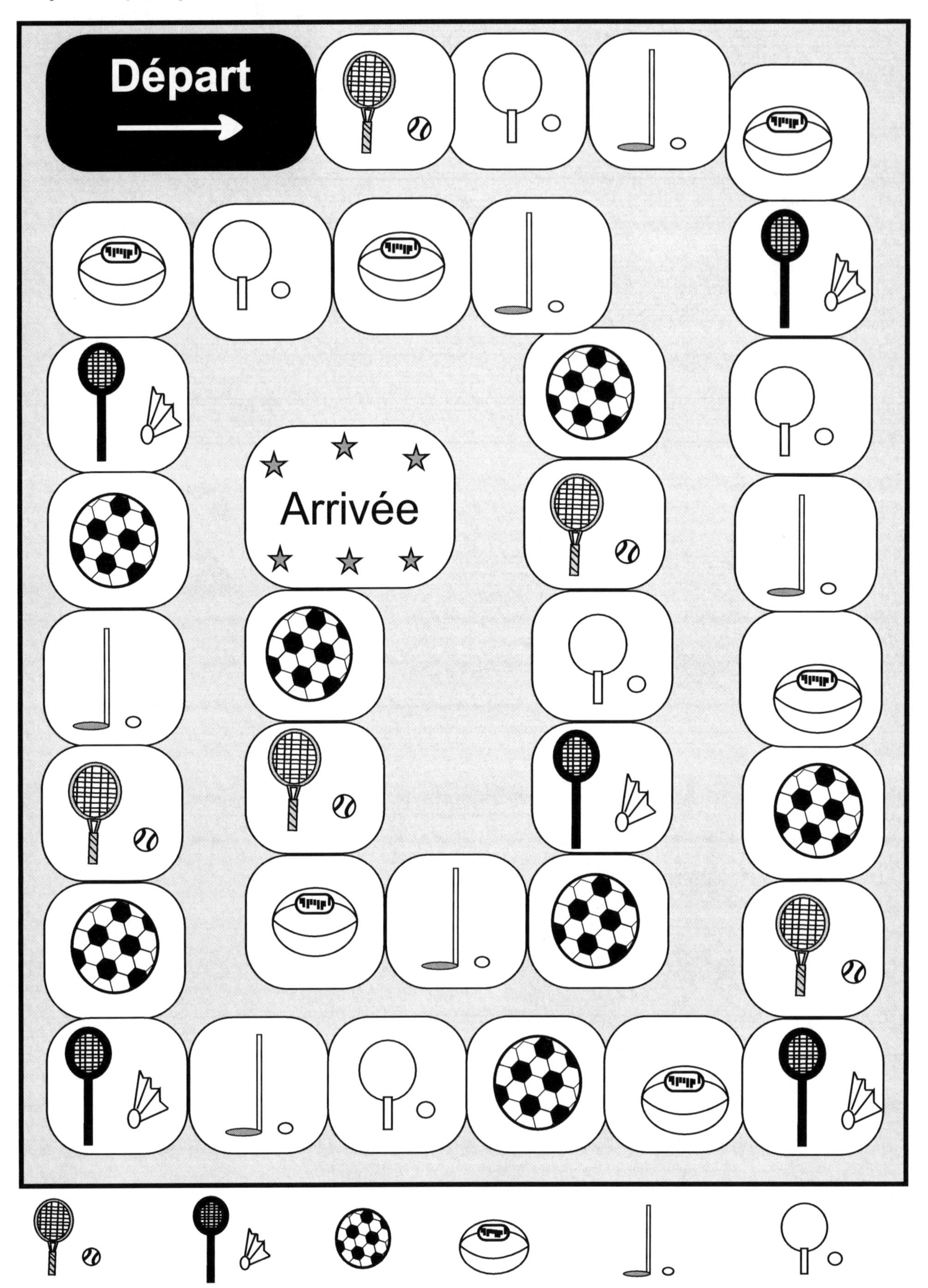

le tennis le badminton le football le rugby le mini-golf le ping-pong

Can I say 9 types of sport?

Each person / team needs 5 coloured counters or cubes of one colour (or a set of noughts or a set of crosses).
Say the French word for the sport as you place your counter.
To win you have to get 3 in a row (vertically, horizontally or diagonally).

le tennis

le badminton

le karaté

le basket

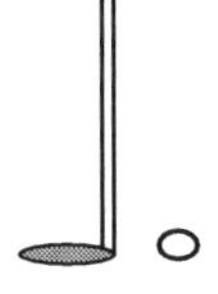
le mini-golf

le football

le rugby

le ping-pong

la natation

Can I say 9 types of sport? - Pupil A

For this game, each person will need 8 domino cards. To make eight domino cards, with an adult cut along the dotted lines. Then, take turns to put a card down by matching a word to a picture or vice versa. If you cannot match a card, miss a turn. The winner is the person to either use all their cards, or use as many cards as possible.

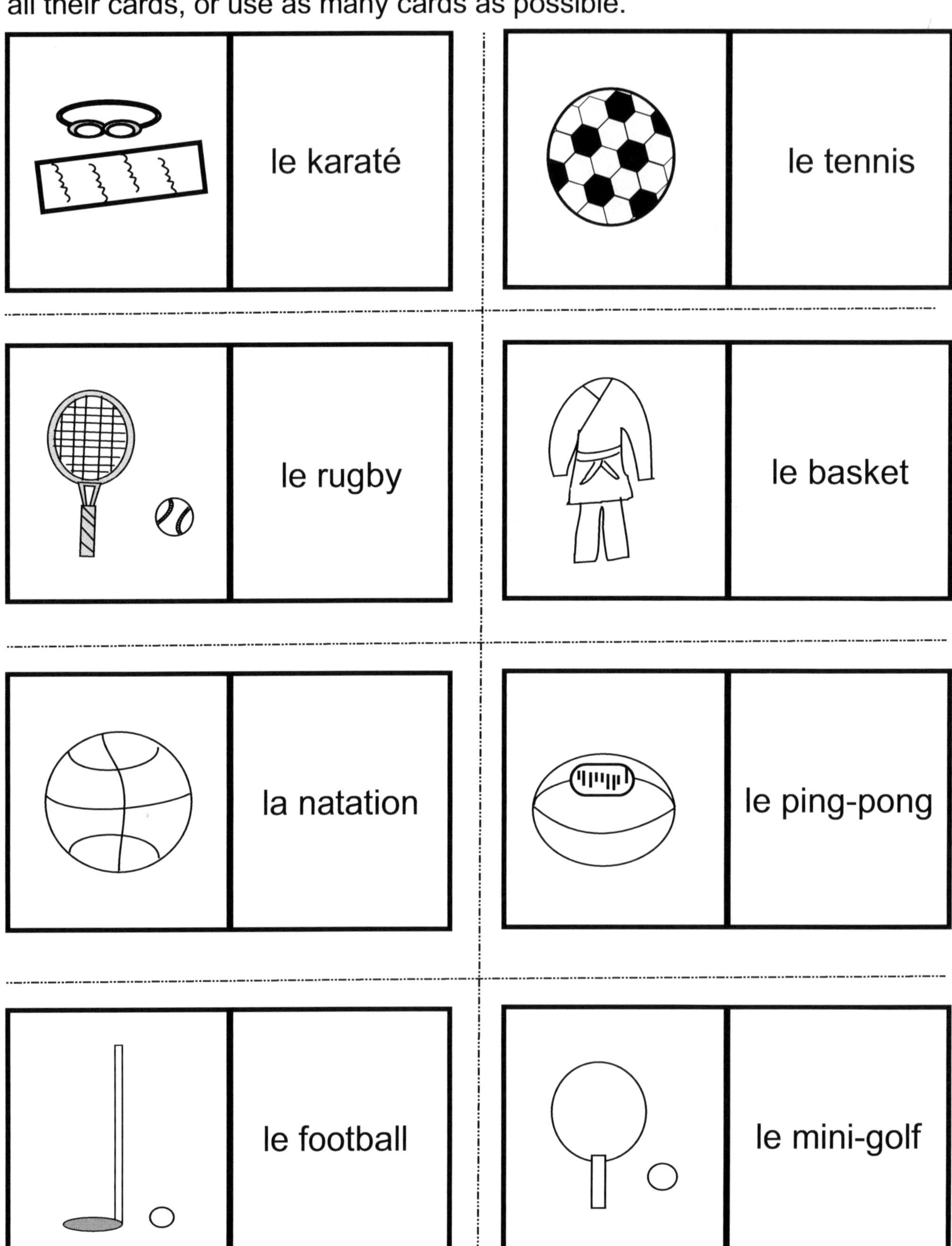

Can I say 9 types of sport? - Pupil B

For this game, each person will need 8 domino cards. To make eight domino cards, with an adult cut along the dotted lines. Then, take turns to put a card down by matching a word to a picture or vice versa. If you cannot match a card, miss a turn. The winner is the person to either use all their cards, or use as many cards as possible.

■ Can I say 12 sports in French?

Each person / team needs 5 coloured counters or cubes of one colour (or a set of noughts or a set of crosses).
Say the French word for the sport as you place your counter.
To win you have to get 3 in a row (vertically, horizontally or diagonally).

le tennis

le badminton

le karaté

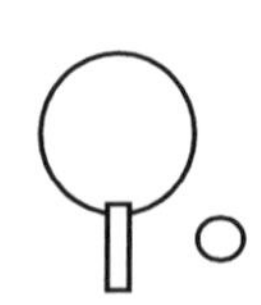

le ping-pong

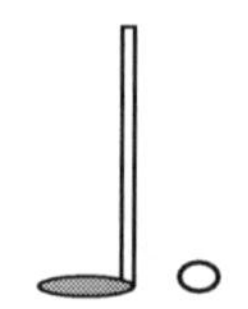

le mini-golf

le basket

le football

le rugby

la natation

le cyclisme

l'équitation

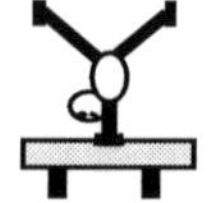

la gymnastique

Can I say 12 sports in French?

Start at "**Départ**", roll the dice and count that number of spaces.
Say the sport you land on in French. To win, arrive first at "Arrivée."

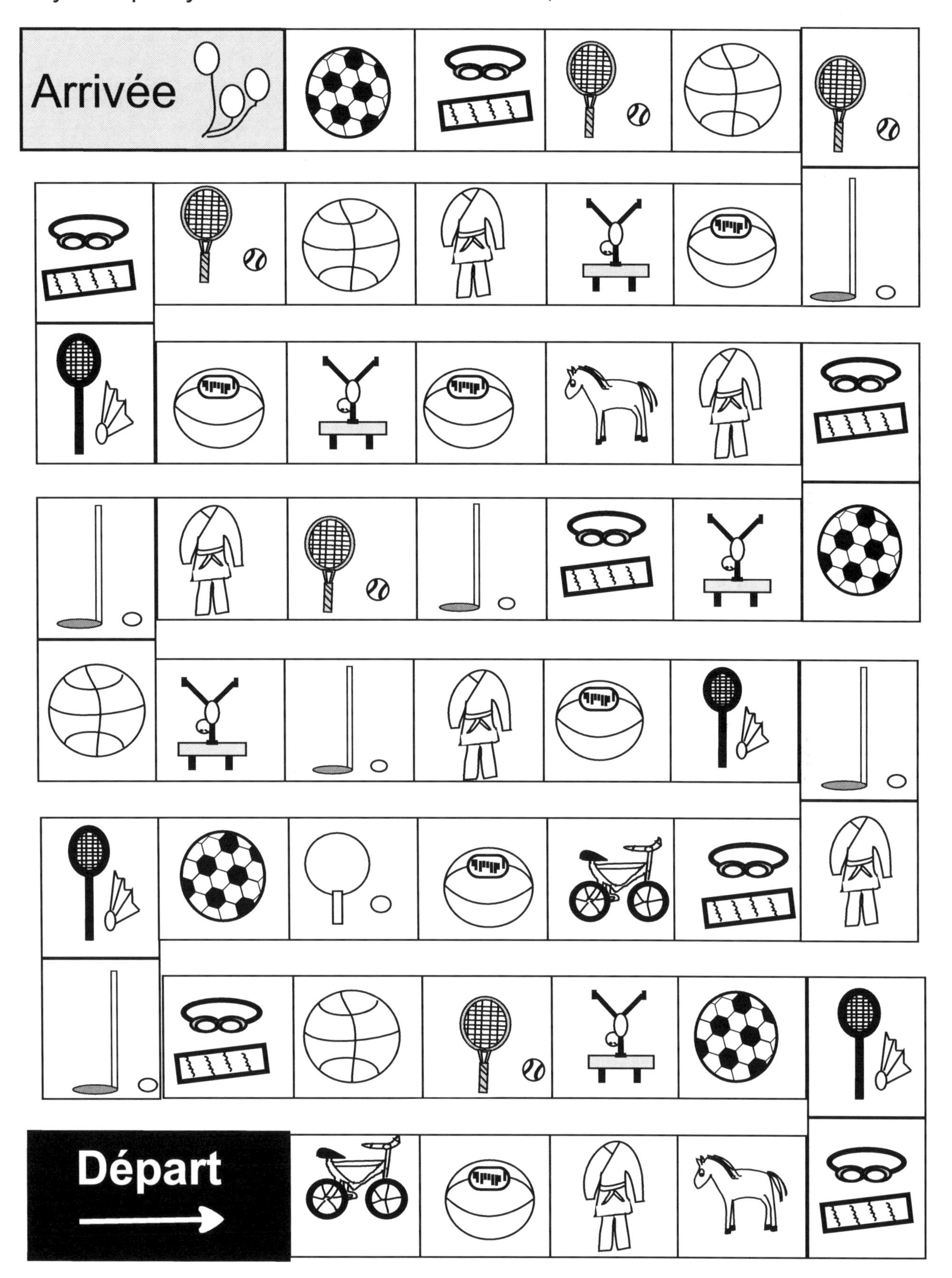

le football le rugby la natation le cyclisme l'équitation la gymnastique

le tennis le basket le badminton le karaté le ping-pong le mini-golf

Making sentences with sports

When the pupils play the games, they could either practise just the vocabulary for the topic, or they could say a whole sentence. Here are some ideas of the sentences you could instruct a group, or the whole class to practise as they play the games:

1) **Giving opinions about which sport you like:**

J'aime = I like e.g. J'aime la natation.

Je n'aime pas = I don't like e.g. Je n'aime pas le rugby.

J'adore = I love e.g. J'adore le football.

Je déteste = I hate e.g. Je déteste le basket.

Je préfère = I prefer e.g. Je préfère le mini-golf.

Mon sport préféré, c'est le = My favourite sport is
e.g. Mon sport préféré, c'est le tennis.

2) **Asking others if they like certain sports:** Tu aimes.....? (Do you like.....?)
E.g. Tu aimes le mini-golf? Tu aimes la natation?

3) **Saying which sports you play**: Je joue au (I play - used for the sports which use a ball or a shuttlecock.) Explain to the pupils they need to change **le** to **au**
e.g. Je joue au football, Je joue au rugby, Je joue au tennis

For the sports which do not use a ball or a shuttlecock, teach the following:
Je fais de la natation (I swim), Je fais de l'équitation (I go horse riding),
Je fais du karaté (I do karate)

4) **Saying when you play various sports**: Ask the pupils to make up a sentence saying when they do a particular sport.

a) **Using the days of the week**:
le lundi = on Mondays, le mardi = on Tuesdays, le mercredi = on Wednesdays
le jeudi = on Thursdays, le vendredi = on Fridays, le samedi = on Saturdays
le dimanche = on Sundays
E.g. Le lundi je joue au basket. Le dimanche je joue au football.

b) **Using seasons**:
En été = in summer En hiver = in winter
En été je joue au tennis. En hiver je joue au badminton.

5) **Asking others if they play various sports**: For a conversation, it is important to know how to ask questions:

Tu joues au = Do you play....? (for sports which use a ball or shuttlecock.)
Tell the pupils the word **le** which appears before the sport changes to **au**.
E.g. Tu joues au football? Tu joues au tennis?

For the other sports ask:
Tu fais de la natation? (Do you swim?) Tu fais du karaté? (Do you do karate?)
Tu fais de l'équitation? (Do you go horse riding?)

Photocopiable word lists

These word lists can be photocopied for the pupils, to either learn for homework or to be stuck in the pupil's workbooks for future reference. They could also be used when playing the mini card games. The words are arranged so the words for "les verts" appear first, then after a space are the extra words for "les jaunes", and all the words listed are for "les rouges."

un chat .... a cat
un chien ...... a dog
un poisson ... a fish
un serpent ... a snake

un lapin .... a rabbit
un cheval .... a horse

un oiseau .... a bird
une tortue .... a tortoise
une souris ... a mouse

les chats ....cats
les chiens ....dogs
les poissons ....fishes
les serpents.....snakes

les lapins ....rabbits
les chevaux ....horses

les oiseaux......birds
les tortues ...... tortoises
les souris .... mice

un coca ....a coke
un jus d'orange ....an orange juice
une limonade ....a lemonade
une eau minérale ....mineral water

un café ....a coffee
un thé ....a tea

un coca light ....a diet coke
un jus de pomme ....an apple juice

1	2	3	4	5	6	7	8	9	10	11	12
un	deux	trois	quatre	cinq	six	sept	huit	neuf	dix	onze	douze

un kiwi ....a kiwi
un melon ....a melon
une orange ....an orange
une pomme ...an apple

une banane ...a banana
une fraise ......a strawberry

un citron ....a lemon
une poire ......a pear
des cerises ... some cherries

kiwis...........kiwis
melons.........melons
oranges ....oranges
pommes ......apples

bananes.......bananas
fraises ....strawberries

citrons.........lemons
poires ....pears
cerises ....cherries

un jean ....jeans
un t-shirt ....a t-shirt
un pull ....a jumper
un manteau ......a coat

un short ....shorts
une jupe ....a skirt

un pantalon ......trousers
une robe ....a dress
une casquette ...a cap

le poisson..............fish
les pommes frites ...chips
les pâtes .... pasta
le gâteau .... cake

la salade .... salad
le poulet ....chicken

le fromage ....cheese
les légumes .... vegetables

le tennis .... tennis
le rugby .... rugby
le football .... football
le mini-golf .... mini-golf
le ping-pong ...... table tennis
le badminton ..... badminton

le basket .... basketball
la natation .... swimming

le karaté............ karate
le cyclisme .... cycling
l'équitation .... horse riding
la gymnastique... gymnastics

rouge ....red
bleu ....blue
jaune ....yellow
vert.............green

noir ....black
blanc ....white
marron ....brown
rose.............pink

violet..........lilac
gris.............grey
orange ....orange
argent ....silver

Pair work activities using the mini cards

The idea of these games is to speak French, so remember to speak French as you enjoy the games. You may choose one of these games:

Pairs card game

Place all the cards face down on the table. With a partner, take turns to turn over two cards.

If you find a matching pair you "win" the cards.

The idea of the game is to try and find as many pairs as possible. Say the French words for the cards as you turn over the cards.

Guess the card

In pairs, each person takes a card. Make sure your partner does not see your card! Take turns to guess each other's card.

If you guess the card correctly, you "win" the card. Each person then takes a new card. Take turns to guess each other's card. The winner is the person who wins the most cards.

I went to the market and bought.....

In pairs, take it in turns to say **il y a** (there is), then add a card of your own choice and place this card face down on the table.

The next person has to repeat **il y a** and the previous card or cards that were said before saying **et** (and) and then their choice of word, and placing this word also face down next to the previous card or cards.

Try not to look at the cards that are face down on the table unless you need to check the word after it has been said.

E.g. Person A : il y a une pomme
Person B : il y a une pomme et une fraise
Person A : il y a une pomme, une fraise et une banane

Qu'est-ce que c'est? (What is it?)

Put all the cards together in a pile, and shuffle the cards. Take it in turns with a partner to take a card:
If it is a picture card, say the French word for the card.
If it is a French word, say what it means in English.

If you know the word you "win" the card. If you don't know the word put the card in a separate pile and at the end of the game check what it means. The idea of the game is to win as many cards as possible.

Guess the word for the picture!

In pairs, pupil A takes a card and draws a picture for this word on a whiteboard. Pupil B has to guess in French the word. Then swap roles.

C'est masculin ou féminin?

(Is it masculine or feminine?)

Using the mini cards, arrange the cards according to if the words are masculine (boy words) or feminine (girl words).

Masculine words start with either **un** (a) or **le** (the)

Feminine words start with either **une** (a) or **la** (the)

(Any words which start with none of the above place in a separate pile.)

Les opinions (opinions)

Take turns to turn over a mini card and say if you like or dislike the thing pictured:

J'aime .... I like

Je n'aime pas........ I don't like

Et toi? .... And you?

For colours you need the word **le** before the colour, but for orange or argent it needs to be **l'** as the words start with a vowel.

For the animals and the fruit the words need to be in the plural when you say your opinion.

Snap

Divide the cards equally between 2 people. Take turns to say the French word for the card as you place the card face up on the table. You will need to make a pile of cards each so that you can see if two cards are the same.

If the two top cards are the same, to win both piles of cards you have to be the first person to say the French word for the top card as you place your hand down on the pile of cards.

Championships

Working as a class or in table groups, two pupils compete at the same time to translate the word first from French to English, or vice versa. The two pupils who are competing stand up by their chair, and they do not need to put up their hand to answer as they can just call out the answer. One person has the mini cards and says whatever is on the top card. Whoever says the word first out of the two competitors stays on, and a new person then stands up to take on the winner. Time the game, and after 5 minutes, whoever wins the final round is the champion.

Mimes

Sport or Animals topic: In pairs, take it in turns to take a card to mime the sport or animal for your partner to guess in French.

Which one is missing?

Put all the picture cards face up on the table. Pupil A closes their eyes and pupil B takes away one card. Pupil A has to say which card is missing in French. Then swap roles.

Teacher's note: Choose how many words you want each group of children to practise, and give the pupils the mini cards for their group, or ask the children to find their words from the whole set they are given. See page 1 for ideas of how to differentiate the topics to three levels. Then, either instruct them an activity to do, or photocopy the above instructions. The pupils will need two sets of cards for the dominoes or pairs card game.

Class activities using the mini cards

Find the matching card

Give the pupils a card each and then ask them to circulate in the room saying the French word for their card. The pupils need to find either the person who has the picture card for their word card, and vice versa, or the person with the same card.

This game can use either just one topic (but have several cards for each word so there are enough cards for the whole class or group) or can be used as revision for various topics. Once the pupils have found a match they could either get a new card from the teacher, or be asked to sit down and draw and label their word on a whiteboard.

Faire du shopping

Half of the class are shop assistants and have the mini cards for the fruit, drinks, food, pets or clothes. The other half are customers. Customers have to circulate in the room asking the shop assistants for one of their cards.
Customers can ask for the card:

by adding **s'il vous plaît** (please) after the French word

Or by saying **Je voudrais .... s'il vous plaît** (I would like ...please)

Montrez-moi (show me)

In table groups / as a whole class everyone has a set of mini cards.

The teacher says **Montrez-moi** then one of the French words.
The pupils compete to be the first to hold up the correct card.

If you are playing this game with the whole class you can differentiate this activity by giving the pupils the cards for the suggested key words for their group (vert, jaune, rouge) as shown at the front of this book on page 1. Then, before you say Montrez-moi, you could tell the class if this time it's for les verts / les jaunes / les rouges.

Written activity

Ask the pupils to randomly choose a mini card and then write a sentence in French on a whiteboard / in their book. Tell the pupils if any of the mini cards appear twice, they do not need to do the sentence again.)

Les maths

The teacher says a simple maths equation, and the class has to hold up the card which is that answer.

E.g. deux plus deux (2 + 2)
answer: quatre

Also available by Joanne Leyland:

French
Young Cool Kids Learn French
Cool Kids Speak French (books 1, 2 & 3)
French Word Games - Cool Kids Speak French
40 French Word Searches Cool Kids Speak French
First 100 Words In French Coloring Book Cool Kids Speak French
Cool Kids Speak French - Special Christmas Edition
Photocopiable Games For Teaching French
On Holiday In France Cool Kids Speak French
Cool Kids Do Maths In French
Un Alien Sur La Terre
Le Singe Qui Change De Couleur
Tu As Un Animal?

Italian
Young Cool Kids Learn Italian
Cool Kids Speak Italian (books 1, 2 & 3)
Italian Word Games - Cool Kids Speak Italian
40 Italian Word Searches Cool Kids Speak Italian
First 100 Words In Italian Coloring Book Cool Kids Speak Italian
On Holiday In Italy Cool Kids Speak Italian
Photocopiable Games For Teaching Italian
Un Alieno Sulla Terra
La Scimmia Che Cambia Colore
Hai Un Animale Domestico?

German
Young Cool Kids Learn German
Cool Kids Speak German (books 1, 2 & 3)
German Word Games - Cool Kids Speak German
40 German Word Searches Cool Kids Speak German
First 100 Words In German Coloring Book Cool Kids Speak German

Spanish
Young Cool Kids Learn Spanish
Cool Kids Speak Spanish (books 1, 2 & 3)
Spanish Word Games - Cool Kids Speak Spanish
40 Spanish Word Searches Cool Kids Speak Spanish
First 100 Words In Spanish Coloring Book Cool Kids Speak Spanish
Cool Kids Speak Spanish - Special Christmas Edition
Photocopiable Games For Teaching Spanish
On Holiday In Spain Cool Kids Speak Spanish
Cool Kids Do Maths In Spanish
Un Extraterrestre En La Tierra
El Mono Que Cambia De Color
Seis Mascotas Maravillosas

English as a foreign language
Cool Kids Speak English (books 1 & 2)

For more information on the books available, and different ways of learning a foreign language go to https://**learnforeignwords.com**